The Tables of the Law tells the story of the early life of Moses, of his preparations for leading his people out of Egypt, of the exodus itself and incidents at the oasis Kadesh, and of the engraving of the stone tables of the law at "Sinai." This story, one of the most dramatic and significant in the Bible, has been given new life and meaning in the richly evocative prose of Thomas Mann. Like *Joseph and His Brothers*, it represents Mann's art at its best.

Thomas Mann's Masterpiece:

Joseph and His Brothers

A Tetralogy comprising:

1.   **Joseph and His Brothers**

2.   **Young Joseph**

3.   **Joseph in Egypt**

4.   **Joseph the Provider**

All four volumes translated by H. T. Lowe-Porter

"No contemporary reader can afford not

to know what is in Thomas Mann's version of

the life of Joseph." . . . Time Magazine

Alfred A. Knopf, Publisher

The	•
Tables	•
Of	•
The	•
Law	•

Translated by H. T. Lowe-Porter

Thomas Mann:

The Tables
Of The LAW.

Alfred A. Knopf......New York

1
9
4
5

Published simultaneously in Canada by The Ryerson Press
Manufactured in the United States of America

The Tables of the Law first appeared in a translation made by
George R. Marek in a volume entitled The Ten Commandments, published
by Simon & Schuster in 1943. The present translation
by H. T. Lowe-Porter copyright 1945 by Alfred A. Knopf, Inc.

The German text Das Gesetz copyright 1944 by Bermann-Fischer Verlag,
Stockholm. Das Gesetz was also published in 1944 in an edition
of 500 copies by Privatdruck der Pazifischen Presse: Los Angeles.

The	•
Tables	•
Of	•
The	•
Law	•

1. His birth was irregular, hence it was he passionately loved order, the absolute, the shalt and shalt not.

In his youth, in a blazing fit of rage, he had killed a man; so he knew, better than the innocent, that to kill is very fine but to have killed is most horrible, and that it is forbidden to kill.

His senses were hot, so he craved the spiritual, the pure, the holy; he craved the unseen, because he felt that the unseen was spiritual, holy and pure.

Among the Midianites, a scattered desert folk, brisk and enterprising shepherds and traders, with whom after the slaying he had taken refuge, fleeing from Egypt the land of his birth (more of that presently) — among the Midianites he had heard of a God you could not see but who saw you, a mountain-dweller who at the same time sat invisible on a movable chest in a tent, where he dispensed oracles by the casting of lots. To the children of Midian this numen, named Jahwe, was merely one god amongst others. They made no great fuss of him, doing his service by way of precaution and just in case. It had struck them that among all the gods there might quite possibly be one whom they did not see, one without a shape, so they sacrificed to him in order not to leave anything out, offend anybody, or draw down unpleasantness from any quarter whatever.

Moses, on the contrary, by reason of his craving for the pure and holy, was deeply impressed by just this feature of Jahwe's invisibility. He felt that no visible god could vie in sanctity with one not visible, and he was amazed that the children of Midian set so little store by a quality which seemed to him so full of incalculable implications. He pondered long and weightily as he kept sheep in the desert for the brother of his Midianitic wife, shaken by inspirations and revelations which, in one instance, even issued out of his own breast and took shape in a blazing outward vision, a proper manifestation laying down the law, inexorably prescribing the task before him. And he arrived at the conviction that Jahwe was no other than El Elyon, the Unique and Highest, El roi, God Who seeth me — He who was already called El Shaddei, the God of the Mountain, El olam, the God of the world and of the eternities — in a word, no other than the

God of Abraham, Isaac, and Jacob, the God of the Fathers and, by inference, of the fathers of the poor benighted folk that dwelt in the land of Egypt. They were enslaved, their traditions forgotten, their worship utterly disorganized; yet it was their very blood that on the father's side flowed in Moses' own veins.

Full of his discovery, with heavy-laden soul, quivering with eagerness to fulfil the command, Moses ended his many years' sojourn among the Midianites. His wife Zipporah, a woman of gentle birth, daughter of Reuel, priest-king in Midian, and sister of Reuel's herd-owning son Jethro, he set on an ass, together with his two sons Gershom and Eliezer, and took the seven days' journey westward through many deserts back into Egypt — or rather into the low-lying fallow land where the Nile divides and where in the district of Kos, also called Goshen, Gosen, and Gosem, dwelt the blood of his father, toiling and moiling.

And straightway wherever he went, into huts and work-sheds and brick-yards, he began to explain to his father's blood this great discovery of his. His arms dangled along his sides and his fists shook in a way they had when he talked. He gave them to know that the God of their fathers was found anew; that He had made Himself known to him, Moshe ben Amram, on Mount Horeb in the desert of Sin, out of a flame of fire in the midst of a bush which burned and was not consumed. And told him that He was called Jahwe, which signified I Am That I Am for ever and ever, but likewise a blowing air and a great noise of wind; and that He had a great mind towards their blood and was ready under certain conditions to make a Covenant with them and elect them for His own out of all peoples. The condition was, that they bind themselves to serve Him and to raise up a sworn brotherhood to the unique and imageless service of the invisible God.

And Moses did not cease to din all this into them, his fists shaking on his broad stone-mason's wrists as he harangued. Yet even so he was not quite straight with them, but kept back various things he had in his mind — yes, even the most important thing of all — lest he frighten them and put them off altogether. He said not a word about the implications of invisibility, the spirituality, purity, and sanctity, and he refrained from pointing out that as sworn servants of the Invisible they had got to be a folk set apart, of extra purity and holiness. He kept quiet for fear of alarming them; for this flesh and blood of his father was so downtrodden and debased, so confused in its worship, he mistrusted it even while he loved it. Yes, when he told his people that Jahwe the Invisible had a mind to them, he was ascribing to the Deity and attributing to Him what may have been true of the god but was certainly true of himself: namely, that Moses had a mind to his father's blood, as the stone-mason has a mind to the uncut block out of which he thinks to carve a fine and lofty statue by the work of his hands. Hence his palpitating eagerness, which had filled him on his departure from Midian, together with the weight of the great burden laid on his spirit through the Lord's command.

For the rest, he kept back the second half of the command, which had been twofold. It had been to the effect not only that Moses should tell the tribes about his rediscovery of the God of their fathers and His mind to them; but also that he was to lead them out of the Egyptian house of bondage into freedom and through many deserts into the land of their fathers, the Promised Land. All this was dependent upon the promise and indissolubly bound up with it. God — and freedom to return; the Invisible — and the shaking off of the foreign yoke. For him these were one and the same; but to the people he said naught as yet, because he knew that the second half followed after the first, and also because he hoped that he himself, single-handed, would worm it out of Pharaoh, King of Egypt — to whom he stood in a certain not remote relation.

Perhaps the people did not care for his speech, for he spoke indeed rather badly, often hesitating for the right word. Or perhaps the way his fists shook made them guess that there was more to be said about the invisibility and the Covenant he offered and that he might be luring them on to dangerous courses beyond their strength. Anyhow, they betrayed a lack of enthusiasm. When he persisted they looked worried and stubborn, glanced towards their Egyptian gaolers, and muttered between their teeth:

"Why are you shouting like that? And what sort of things are you blurting out? And who made you a prince and a judge over us? We would not know."

That was no news to him. He had heard it before, when he fled to Midian.

2. His father was not his father, and his mother was not his mother — so irregular had been his birth. One day Ramessu the Pharaoh's second daughter was disporting herself with her maidens in the royal gardens on the Nile, protected by armed guards. She saw a Hebrew slave drawing water, and she lusted after him. His eyes were sad, he had a new little beard on his chin, and you could see the muscles on his arms when he drew up the water. He laboured in the sweat of his brow, and his troubles were many; but to Pharaoh's daughter he was a dream of beauty and desire. And she ordered him to be sent to her into her pavilion. She ran her exquisite little white hands through his sweat-damp locks, kissed the muscles of his arms, and aroused his manhood until he took her — he, the foreign slave, took the child of the king. When he had had her she let him go. But he went not far. After thirty paces he was cut down and straightway buried, and the sun-daughter's pleasure was at an end.

"Poor thing!" she said when she heard. "You are all so officious. He would have kept quiet; he loved me." But she proved to be with child, and in nine months, though no one knew it, she bore a man-child, and her women put him in a little basket of rushes coated with pitch and hid it in the reeds at the edge of the water. After a while they found it there and made outcry, saying: "Oh, a miracle, a foundling exposed in the rushes, just like the old fairy-tales, where Akki the water-bearer finds Sargon in the reeds and brings him up in the goodness of his heart. It happens over and over. But what shall we do with our find?

The most sensible thing would be to give him to a nursing mother of humble birth who has more than enough milk, and let him grow up as the son of her and her good husband." And they gave the child to a Hebrew woman, who took it down to the land of Goshen to Jochebed, wife of Amram, one of the Hebrew emigrés, a man of the house of Levi. She was suckling her own son Aaron and had too much milk. Moreover, she profited now and then by good things sent to her house from an exalted source. So in the goodness of her heart she brought up the nameless child with her own. Thus Amram and Jochebed became Moses' parents before men, and Aaron was his brother. Amram had fields and herds, and Jochebed was the daughter of a stonemason. They did not know what to call the unlikely little lad; in the end they gave him a half-Egyptian name, or rather half of an Egyptian name. For the sons of the land were often named Ptah-mose, Amen-mose, or Ra-mose: in other words, sons of those gods. Amram and Jochebed preferred to leave out the god-name and simply called the boy Mose, or just "son." The question was, Whose?

3. He grew up as a member of the migrant tribe and spoke in their tongue. Their forefathers had been allowed into Egypt at the time of a drought: "hungry Bedouins from Edom," Pharaoh's clerks called them. The frontier authorities had passed them into the land of Goshen, and the lowland had been given them for pasturage. If anyone imagine they could have pastured there under any other circumstances, he does not know the children of Egypt, their hosts. Not only had they to pay such high taxes on their cattle that it was a grievous burden; but all those strong enough among them had to give their labour as well: they had to work on the building operations of all sorts that were always going on in a country like Egypt. Particularly since Ramessu,

second of his name, had been on the throne in Thebes, extrava-
gant building had been his pleasure and his royal delight. Mag-
nificent and costly temples he built all over the land, and down
below in the Delta he not only widened and improved the long-
neglected canal that connected the eastern branch of the Nile
with the Bitter Lakes and thus linked the Great Sea with the tip
of the Red Sea, but also he built two great warehouse cities at
the edge of the canal, called Pithom and Raamses. And now the
children of the immigrants, these Ibrim, were conscripted to
bake bricks, to haul and stack them in the sweat of their bodies
beneath the Egyptian rod.

This rod of Pharaoh's overseers was more symbolic than
functional: the tribes were not wantonly beaten with it. And the
labourers ate well: plenty of fish from the Nile branch, bread,
beef and beer enough and to spare. But even so such toil was
not in their line. They were of nomad stock, traditionally of a
free and roving life. Work by the hour, till they sweated, went
against their grain. But they could not get together over their
grievances, not being enough aware of themselves as a group.
Generation after generation they had tented in a transitional
land between the home of their fathers and Egypt proper. Their
souls were unformed, their spirits wavering, and of settled
teaching they had none. They had forgotten much, half-remem-
bered more; lacking in steadiness, they were also without belief
in themselves, so that even their resentment was feeble and
yielded readily to all the free fish and beef and beer.

Now Moses, passing for Amram's son, would probably have
had to make bricks for Pharaoh like the rest as soon as he grew
out of childhood. But that did not happen. For the youth was
removed from his parents and sent to Upper Egypt to a sort of
elegant boarding-school where the sons of Syrian city kings
were brought up together with scions of the native nobility.
Thither he was sent. For his real mother, Pharaoh's daughter,
who had borne him into the reeds, a loose female enough to be
sure, but not at all spiritless, had been mindful of him for the
sake of his buried father, the sad-eyed water-bearer with the little beard. She wanted him not to continue with the desert folk,

but to be educated as an Egyptian and granted a Court appoint-
ment, by way of recognizing, even secretly, his divine blood on
one side. So then Moses, dressed in white linen with a wig on
his head, learned about countries and heavenly bodies, writing
and the law. But he was not happy among the young fops in the
elegant boarding-school. He was a solitary among them, full of
distaste for all the Egyptian refinements and the luxury to which
in fact he owed his being. The blood of the buried one who had
had to serve that luxury was stronger in him than the Egyptian
half, and his soul held with the poor unformed ones in Goshen
who had not even the courage of their resentments. He held
with them against the looseness and empty pride of his mother's
side.

"What is your name?" his schoolmates might ask him.

"Moses," he answered.

"Ahmose or Ptahmose?" they asked.

"Just Moses," he replied.

"That is very low, it is common and ugly," said the swagger-
ing youth. And Moses was so enraged he would have liked to
kill and bury them. For he knew that their questions were aimed
at his illegitimate birth, of which everybody was vaguely in-
formed. How could he not know that he was only a by-blow,
the fruit of Egyptian luxury, when it was accepted though not
very specific fact in all circles, even the highest — the dal-
liance of his daughter being as little of a secret from Pharaoh
as it was from Moses himself — that Ramessu the builder was
his grandfather in the pleasant flesh, issue of a passion both
loose and fatal? Yes, Moses knew it and knew that Pharaoh
knew it; and when he thought of it he nodded threateningly in
the direction of the throne.

4. After he had lived two years among the dandies of the Theban
school, he could stand it no longer. He climbed the wall and ran

away at night, and bent his steps homewards to Goshen to his father's kin. He moved about morosely among the tribes. One day by the canal, near Ramessu's new buildings, he saw an Egyptian overseer strike down with his staff one of the labourers who had probably been idle or stubborn. Moses went white. With blazing eyes he accosted the Egyptian, who for all answer hit him on the nose, so that the bone was smashed in and remained so all his life. But Moses snatched the overseer's staff and fetched him a frightful blow which broke the man's skull and killed him on the spot. He had not once looked round to see if anyone saw him. But it was a lonely spot; no one was near. So he buried the man alone, for he whom he had defended had fled; and after the slaying and burying he felt as though it was what he had always wanted.

His deed of violence remained hidden, at least from the Egyptians: they did not find out what had become of the overseer, and time passed. Moses kept moving about among his father's people, and annoyed them by meddling in their affairs. One day he saw two labourers of the Ibrim quarrelling and nearly coming to blows. "What is the matter with you, quarrelling and almost fighting?" he said. "Aren't you wretched and forlorn enough to stick together, instead of showing your teeth at each other? This man is wrong; I saw it. Let him yield and be content, and as for the other, let him not be stiff-necked."

But, as will often happen, suddenly they turned on him together, saying: "Why are you mixing in our affairs?" And the man Moses found in the fault was the more impudent of the two and shouted: "Well, that is the limit! Who are you to stick your goat's nose into things that don't concern you? Aha, you are Moses, son of Amram, but that is not saying much, for nobody really knows who you are, not even yourself. We are curious to know who made you a prince and a judge over us. Do you mean to kill me as you killed the Egyptian?"

"Be quiet!" said Moses in alarm. But to himself he thought: How did this become known? So next day he saw what he must do, and he crossed the border where it was not closed, by the

Bitter Lakes, through the reedy shallows. Through many deserts of the land of Sinai he came to Midian, to the Minaeans and their priest-king Reuel.

5. When he returned to Egypt, filled with his discovery of God and with his mission, he was a robust man at the height of his powers; with flattened nose, prominent cheek-bones, a beard parted in the middle, wide-set eyes, and wrists that had a striking breadth about them, as one could see particularly when he covered his mouth and beard with his right hand, musing, as he often did. He went from hut to hut and work-shed to work-shed, shook his fists alongside his thighs, and spoke of the Invisible, the God of the Fathers expectant of the Covenant. But although he talked much, at bottom he could not talk. For his was altogether a pent-up, inhibited nature, and in excitement he inclined to be tongue-tied. Moreover, he was not perfectly at home in any language and blundered about in all three when he talked. The Aramaic Syro-Chaldaean spoken by his father's people and learned from his parents had been overlaid by the Egyptian tongue he had had to conform to in school. Then there was the Midianitic Arabic he had used so long in the desert. He mixed them all up together.

His brother Aaron was very useful to him: a tall, mild man with a black beard, black locks in the back of his neck, and large full eyelids which he kept piously cast down. Moses had initiated him into all the mysteries and won him over completely for the Invisible, with all its implications. And as Aaron knew how to give tongue with fluency and unction from his bearded lips, he mostly went where Moses went on his mission of conversion and spoke in Moses' place. His voice to be sure was rather guttural and oily, and did not carry full conviction; so that Moses was always trying to contribute more fire to Aaron's words, shaking his fists and often interrupting in his own helter-skelter jargon of Arabic, Aramaic, and Egyptian.

Aaron's wife was named Elisheba, the daughter of Amminadab. She too was strong for the Covenant and the teaching, and so was Miriam, a younger sister of Moses and Aaron, a woman fired by the spirit, who could play on the timbrel and sing. But more than all these Moses favoured a certain youth who for his part supported Moses body and soul in all his preaching and plans and stirred not from his side. His name was actually Hosea, son of Nun (which means fish) of the tribe of Ephraim; but Moses had given him the Jahwe-name of Jehoshua, or Joshua for short, and he wore it proudly — an upright, muscular young man with a curly head, prominent Adam's apple, and two distinct deep folds between his brows. In this whole business he had his peculiar point of view, and it was not so much religious as military. For to Joshua, Jahwe the God of their fathers was above all the God of battles, and the idea of escaping from the house of bondage had as a necessary sequel the conquest of new habitations for the Hebrew tribes. Somewhere they had to live; and no land, whether promised or not, would be just given to them.

Joshua, young as he was, had all the facts in that curly head of his that sat so straight on his shoulders and looked so directly out of its eyes. He discussed them endlessly with Moses, his elder, master, and friend. Without commanding the means for an exact census, Joshua had estimated that the strength of the tented tribes in Goshen and the factory towns of Pithom and Raamses, adding in the Hebrew slaves scattered throughout the country, might be around twelve or thirteen thousand souls in all. Their numbers were afterwards exaggerated out of all reason; but Joshua knew them with fair accuracy and was not very well satisfied with the figure. Three thousand men was no great strength, even if you reckoned that once on the way their numbers would be likely to be increased by the adhesion of various vaguely allied stocks now roving about in the desert. But with no greater resources than these no large enterprises could be thought of; it would be impossible with no greater numbers to

thrust forward into the Promised Land. Joshua could see as
much; therefore his immediate hope was for some free space
where the tribes could settle down and be left for a while under
fairly favourable circumstances to their normal rate of increase,
which, as Joshua knew his people, meant two and a half to every hundred each year. So the youth was looking for covert and
coverture, a retreat where more military strength could be bred
and built up. He often discussed his ideas with Moses, display-
ing a clear knowledge of geography, for he had a sort of map
in his head of the suitable sites, with distances and water sup-
plies. He even knew who dwelt in them, and how militant the
inhabitants were.

Moses well knew what he had in his Joshua; knew that he
would need him, and loved his zeal, although its immediate ob-
jects interested him but little. Covering mouth and beard with
his right hand, he listened to the youth's strategic outgivings,
his mind dwelling on other matters the while. For Moses too,
Jahwe meant, of course, the exodus; but not so much as a cam-
paign to conquer land as a journey into freedom and segrega-
tion. Jahwe meant that he, Moses, would have to himself all this
helpless, hapless flesh and blood, now hanging confused among
many cultures, all these begetting men and childing women,
groping youth and children with running noses, his father's own
blood, in a place somewhere outside in the open to stamp upon
them the holy invisible God, the pure and spiritual; to gather
them into a nucleus and shape them in His image. They should
put on a folk-shape distinct from all others, belonging to God,
destined for the holy and spiritual life, distinguished from all
others by reverence, awe, and abstention — in other words by
fear before the ideas of purity, precept, and discipline. And
since the Invisible was in truth the God of all the world, that
fear would in the future bind all humanity; but first of all it
would be proclaimed for them alone and be their claim to
power among the heathen.

Such was Moses' mind to his father's blood. It was the mind
of the maker, which to him was identical with God's favour and
election, His zeal for the Covenant. He was convinced that this

formative interlude must take precedence of all the enterprises which young Joshua had in his head. And for that purpose time was needed — free time outside in the open; so he did not mind the delay in Joshua's plans due to insufficient numbers of arms-bearing men. Joshua needed time, first for the tribes to multiply according to nature, and secondly in order that he himself might put on more years and be in a position to lead the armies when formed. And Moses needed time to form their souls, a divine work which in his own very soul he craved to commence. So from their different points of view Moses and Joshua were at one.

6. In the meantime he on whom the task was laid, together with his nearest followers, the eloquent Aaron, Elisheba, Miriam, Joshua, and a certain Caleb, of the same age as Joshua, and his bosom-friend — a simple, brave, straightforward young man — in the meantime all these wasted not a moment, but went about spreading among their kin the gospel of Jahwe the Invisible and His flattering offer of the Covenant. At the same time they fomented the resentment of the tribes against their Egyptian task-masters and laboured to spread the idea of shaking off their yoke — the idea of the exodus. Each did it in his own way: Moses with halting words and shaking fists; Aaron with oily eloquence, Elisheba prattling persuasively, Joshua and Caleb with military brusqueness, and Miriam, who soon became known as the prophetess, in loftier vein to the sound of the timbrel. And their preachments did not fall on stony ground. The idea of vowing themselves to Moses' favouring God, of dedicating themselves to the Imageless and going out into freedom under His banner and his prophet's — it took root among them and began to be their united goal; the more so that Moses promised, or at least held out high hopes, that he would deal with the top authorities and get sanction for the exodus out of Egypt, so that it need not be carried out as a dangerous revolt, but in pursuance of an amicable agreement. They knew, vaguely, about Moses' half-Egyptian reed-birth, the aristocratic upbringing he had had in early years, and the personal relations he could command with the Court itself. His mixed blood, his position as it were with one foot in the Egyptian camp, had once been a source of mistrust and dislike. Now it became a cause of confidence and lent him added authority. Certainly he, if anyone, was the man to stand before Pharaoh and lead their enterprise. And so they commissioned him to the office of arranging their departure with Ramessu the builder, their taskmaster. Or rather, they commissioned him and his foster-brother Aaron. For Moses meant to take him along, first because he himself could not speak connectedly and Aaron could, but also because Aaron had a certain magic rod with which they hoped to make play at Court in Jahwe's favour. He could take a cobra and press its neck and make it stiff; then when he threw it to the ground it curled up and turned into a snake again. Neither Moses nor Aaron took account of the fact that Pharaoh's magicians knew the same trick, so that it would scarcely serve as an awe-inspiring instance of Jahwe's might.

They had no luck at all, anyhow; it was not in the cards, however craftily, after a council of war with the youths Joshua and Caleb, they went about it. It had been decided to ask the King merely for permission for the Hebrew people to assemble and go out a three days' journey into the wilderness, to feast and make sacrifice in obedience to the summons of the Lord their God, and then to come back to work. This was merely the mild and polite form of a petition to depart, and it was scarcely to be expected that Pharaoh would be deceived and believe they would come back. Indeed, he did not take kindly to it at all.

But at least the brothers did succeed in standing in the Great House and before Pharaoh's seat, and that not once but many times in the course of stoutly fought and protracted negotiations. Moses had not promised his people too much, standing as he did on the firm ground of his relation to Ramessu, his grandfather in the lust of the flesh. Each knew that the other knew. Thus Moses had in his hand the means of applying pressure. It was never quite strong enough to win the King's consent to the exodus; but it did procure serious attention, and time after time it got him entry to the All-Powerful, because the All-Powerful was afraid of him. Of course, the fear of a King is dangerous, and Moses was playing a dangerous game all the while. He had courage — how much, and what impression he made with it on his people, we shall soon see. Ramessu could easily have had him put out of the way and done away with all trace of his daughter's little side-step. But the princess still had a sweet memory of that quarter-hour's enjoyment and did not want her reed-boy to come to any harm. She went on protecting him, however ungracious his response had been to her plans for his education and advancement.

So Moses and Aaron were permitted to stand before Pharaoh. But the idea of the excursion and sacrifice he curtly brushed aside. In vain Aaron cast down his rod and turned it into a snake; for Pharaoh's magician did the same thing without turning a hair, proving that the Invisible, in whose name the Hebrews spoke, enjoyed no superior authority and that Pharaoh did not need to hearken to the voice of these men.

"Pestilence and the sword will visit our people if we do not go out three days' journey into the desert and sacrifice to the Lord our God." But the King answered: "It moves us not. You are numerous enough — more than twelve thousand head — and could well do with the reduction of your numbers through pestilence and the sword or extreme toil. You, Moses, and Aaron — you are just aiding and abetting your people in idleness and getting them a holiday from the work they owe. I cannot and will not allow it; I have several vast temples in building; moreover, I intend to erect a third warehouse town besides Pithom and Raamses, and I require your people's arms for the work. I thank you for the present interview, and you, Moses, I dismiss, well or ill, with special favour. But let us hear no more talk about celebrations in the desert."

Thus the audience ended. And not only did no good come of it, but in the sequel actual ill. For Pharaoh, affronted in his building zeal and out of sorts because he could not have Moses strangled lest his daughter make trouble for him, ordered that the people of Goshen be more sorely oppressed than ever and the rod not spared when they were idle. They must work the harder to get this idea out of their heads, and all idle thoughts about the feast in the desert should be sweated out of them. And so it was. The work grew daily harder after Moses and Aaron had spoken before Pharaoh. For instance, they got no more straw for the bricks they had to bake, but had to go into the stubble-field to gather what they needed, that the tale of bricks might not be minished. Otherwise the cudgel should dance up and down on their poor backs. In vain the officers of the children of Israel made representations to the authorities. The answer was: "You are idle, idle are you, so you come and say: 'We want to go and make sacrifice.' But the fact remains: get your own straw and deliver the full tale of bricks."

7. For Moses and Aaron it was no small embarrassment. The head men said to them: "There you have it; and this is what we have got for the Covenant with your God and from Moses' connections. You have done nothing but to make a stink in Pharaoh's nostrils and his servants' and give the sword into their hands to slay us."

That was not easy to answer, and Moses had some bad quarter-hours in his private sessions with the God of the thorn-bush, where he represented to Him how he, Moses, had been from the first unwilling to be charged with the mission and had begged not to be sent upon it no matter who else was, since he could not even talk properly. But the Lord had answered him that Aaron was eloquent. So then Aaron had been the spokesman, speaking much too fawningly and showing what a mistake it was to undertake such an affair, for a man who was thick-tongued himself and had to let others speak for him. But God both consoled and rebuked him out of his very own bosom and answered him thence, he should be ashamed of such pusillanimity; moreover, that his excuses had been the sheerest affectation, for at bottom he had been as eager for the mission himself, having as much a mind to the children of Israel and the shaping of them as He, God, had. Yes, that his, Moses', predilection was in nothing different from God's own, being one and the same: it was the God-desire had set him at the work, and he should blush to faint now at the first check.

Moses had borne all this the better that Joshua, Caleb, and Aaron and the excitable women had decided in council that the new set-back, whatever bad blood it made, had not been such a bad beginning when you really looked at it. For the bad blood was not only against Moses, but even more against the Egyptians, and had made the tribes more receptive for the summons of the saviour God and the idea of the exodus into the open. And it was so: the ferment against the straw and the bricks increased among the workers, and the reproach that Moses had made them a stench and only injured them was accordingly forgotten in the desire that Amram's son should exploit his connections further and go again before Pharaoh's throne.

That he did. This time not with Aaron but alone, let his tongue stammer as it would; he shook with his fists, standing before the throne, and demanded with halting and ejaculations permission for the exodus of his people into the free land, under colour of the sacrifice in the desert. Not once he did this, but even ten times, for Pharaoh could not exactly deny him audience, considering all the facts. A hard and prolonged struggle ensued between the King and Moses. Never did it get so far as to convert the King to Moses' view; a more likely result would be that some day the people of Goshen would be thrust out of a land only too glad to see the last of them. About the struggle and the kind of pressure exerted on the stubbornly resisting King, much has been written and said, not without plausibility, though all of it bears the marks of having been embellished. There is talk of the ten plagues, with which Jahwe one after the other afflicted Egypt to soften Pharaoh's heart, while at the same time He deliberately hardened it in order to show His power afresh by ever new plagues. Blood, frogs, vermin, wild beasts, murrain, boils, hail, locusts, darkness, and death of the first-born: these were the ten plagues, and not one of them impossible — though it is a question whether any of them contributed anything to the result excepting the last, which is very obscure and has never been entirely explained. The Nile, under some circumstances, can assume a blood-red colour, its waters are temporarily foul, and the fish die. That happens. It is possible for frogs to multiply in the marshes or lice and flies to propagate to the proportion of a plague. There were still many lions roving at the edge of the desert and lurking in the jungle of the dead branch of the Nile. And if the number of ravening attacks on men and beast were greatly on the increase, that too might be considered a plague. How frequent are itch and mange in Egypt, and how easily there might be eruptions due to uncleanliness which would riot like a pestilence among the masses! In that land the sky is mostly clear; so that a rare and violent storm must make the profounder impression, and the lightning thrust mingled with the coarse gravel of hail strike the crops and make the trees to writhe without having any special significance beyond the natural. The locust is an all-too-familiar guest, and men have sometimes found means of protection against its greedy hosts. Yet oftener they come on triumphant, and whole stretches of land are devoured and laid bare. Finally, whoever has witnessed the gloomy and sinister atmosphere accompanying an eclipse of the sun can understand that a people used to brilliant light might call such a darkness and gloom by the name of plague.

But with that the tale of the plagues is done; for the tenth, the death of the first-born, is not in the same category, being an incident closely connected with the exodus itself, very puzzling and perhaps better left unexamined. As for the others, any of them might have happened singly or, in a long enough span of time, have happened "all together." One has to regard them more or less as figures of speech for the one single form of pressure that Moses could exert against Ramessu: the fact that Pharaoh was his grandfather in the flesh and that Moses could always make it public. More than once the King came close to yielding, and in time he did make great concessions. He consented that the males might go out to the sacrifice and feast, the women and children, flocks and herds remaining behind. Moses did not agree. With young and old, sons and daughters, sheep and oxen they must go out, for this was to be a feast before the Lord. Then Pharaoh yielded the wives and children, keeping back only the cattle for a pledge. But Moses inquired where, if there were no cattle, the animals would come from for the slaughter and the burnt offering. No, not one single hoof might remain behind — and thus it became clear that here was no question of a leave, but of a leaving.

This matter of the cattle resulted in a last stormy scene between Egypt's Majesty and Jahwe's servant. Moses had displayed great patience throughout the interview, though his fists shook with his inward rage. Pharaoh at last brought things to a head and literally drove Moses out of the hall of audience. "Away!" he shouted, "and take care not to come before my face again! If you do you shall die the death." Then Moses, from high excitement got all at once perfectly calm. He answered: "You have said. I go, and I will come no more before your face." But beneath this frightful composure as he took his leave his thoughts were not pleasant to contemplate. He did not like them himself — but the young men, Joshua and Caleb, they did.

8. This is a dark chapter, to be set down only in half-words and veiled. A day came, or rather a night, an evil vesper, when Jahwe, or rather his avenging angel, went about and visited the tenth plague upon the children of Egypt, or rather upon a part of them, the Egyptians among the dwellers in Goshen as well as in the cities of Pithom and Raamses; for those huts and

houses whose door-posts had been marked with blood as a sign were spared and passed by.

What was He doing? He was causing a dying, the dying of the first-born of Egyptian stock — in which He met many secret wishes and helped many second-born to their rights, which might otherwise have been withheld. A distinction must be noted between Jahwe and His avenging angel. It was not Jahwe Himself who went about, but His avenging angel or probably more correctly a whole carefully chosen band of them. But if anybody is bent on reducing the multiplicity to one, then much goes to show that Jahwe's avenging angel took the shape of an upstanding youthful figure with curly hair, prominent Adam's apple, and well-marked brows, a type of angel which is at all times glad to make an end of fruitless negotiations and get down to action.

There had been no lack of preparations for decisive action during the protracted negotiations with Pharaoh. For Moses himself they had been limited to his anticipating serious trouble and sending back his wife and sons secretly to Midian, to his brother-in-law Jethro, so as not to be hampered by concern about them. But Joshua, whose relation to Moses unmistakably resembles that of the avenging angel to Jahwe, had behaved after his own lights; and as he had not the means, or even the authority, to put his three thousand arms-bearing comrades on a war footing, he armed at least a chosen few, drilled them and kept them under discipline, so that in case of need they would do for a start.

The events of that long-ago are shrouded in darkness — in the very darkness of the vesper which, in the eyes of the children of Egypt, was a feast-night for the slaves who lived among them. These slaves, it seemed, wanted to make up for the forbidden sacrificial feast in the desert by a celebration where they were, with feasting, lights, and worship. They had even borrowed gold and silver vessels for the occasion from their Egyptian neighbours. But meanwhile, possibly instead of the feast, there came this going-about of the avenging angel, the death of the first-born in all the houses not marked by the branch of hyssop dipped in blood. The visitation brought with it so great a confusion, such a sudden upset of stable conditions and legal rights, that from one hour to the next the Moses-people found that the way out of the country stood open — yes, and that they could not take it fast enough to please the Egyptians. Actually it seems that the second-born were less zealous to avenge the death of those whose place they took than the originators of their elevation were to depart. The story goes that the ten plagues at last broke Pharaoh's pride so that he let Moses' father's tribe go free from slavery. Yet he sent speedily in pursuit a division of troops, which then were miraculously destroyed.

Be that as it may, in any case the exodus took the form of an expulsion, and the haste in which it was performed is established by the known detail that nobody had time to raise bread for the journey. They could only provide themselves with unleavened cakes, and Moses made the circumstance a commemoration and feast for all time. For the rest, great and small were quite ready. While the avenging angel went about they had sat with girded loins by their loaded carts, their shoes on their feet, their staves in their hands. The gold and silver vessels they had borrowed from the natives they took along.

My friends, in the exodus out of Egypt both killing and stealing took place. But Moses had firmly resolved that it should be for the last time. How shall man rid himself once and for all of sin save by making himself thoroughly sinful to begin with? Moses now had them out in the open — this fleshly object of his pedagogic concern, this formless humanity, his father's blood. In freedom the work of sanctification could begin.

9. The pilgrim band, very much smaller than legend reports, but hard enough to handle, lead, and tend for all that, were quite enough burden for him who bore the responsibility for their fate.

They took the only route they could take if they wanted to avoid the Egyptian fortifications that begin north of the Bitter Lakes. It led through the district of the Salt Lakes, into which runs the larger, more westerly arm of the Red Sea to make a peninsula of the land of Sinai. Moses knew this region; he had passed through it both on his flight to Midian and on his return. Better than to young Joshua, the lie of the land was familiar to Moses, and the nature of these reedy shallows which sometimes made a connection between the Bitter Lakes and the sea, and through which under some conditions one could cross over dry-shod into the land of Sinai. That is, if a strong east wind were blowing, the waters would be driven back and afford free passage. It was in this state the fugitives found them, thanks to Jahwe's favouring dispensation.

Joshua and Caleb spread the news among the hosts that Moses, invoking God, had held his staff above the waters and induced them to withdraw and make a passage for the people. Probably he did hold out his staff, aiding the east wind with solemn gesture in Jahwe's name. Anyhow, the faith of the people in their leader could do with such strengthening, the more that just here, and here first, it was put upon a hard proof. For here it was that Pharaoh's pursuing hosts, troops and waggons, grim sickle-waggons which they knew only too well, overtook the fugitives and came very near to putting a bloody terminus to their pilgrimage to God.

The news of their approach came from Joshua's rear guard and roused extreme panic among the people. Regret that they had followed "this man Moses" flared up at once, and a mass murmuring arose which, to Moses' bitter affliction, was to repeat itself at every fresh difficulty they got into. The women cried to heaven, the men cursed and shook their fists at their thighs just as Moses did when he was outraged. "Were there not graves in Egypt," they said, "where we could have been laid peacefully at our hour, if we had stopped at home?" All at once Egypt was "home," which had always been a foreign house of bondage. "It would be better for us to serve the Egyptians than to perish by the sword in the wilderness." A thousand times Moses heard it;

it even embittered the joy of deliverance, overwhelming as that was. He was always "the man Moses who led us out of Egypt," and that was praise so long as things went right. But if things went wrong, then the tune changed and the words turned into a growl of reproach, from which the idea of stoning was not so remote.

Well, after the brief alarm, things went so incredibly well that the people were abashed. Now Moses, by God's favour, stood very high, and was "the man who led us out of Egypt" — only in the other sense. The tribes rolled through the dry fords, and after them the waggons of Egypt. Then the wind died down, the waters rushed back, man and steed perished with gurgles in the consuming flood.

The triumph was beyond everything. Miriam the prophetess, Aaron's sister, sang, leading the women in the dance: "Sing to the Lord, for He has triumphed gloriously, the horse and his rider has He thrown into the sea." She wrote it herself. It must be imagined sung to the timbrel.

The people were deeply moved. The words mighty, holy, frightful, wonderful, miracle-working did not cease to pour from their lips. And it was unclear whether the adjectives were applied to the Deity or to Moses the man of God, of whom one assumed that his staff had brought the devouring flood rolling back over the might of Egypt. This confusion always threatened. When the people were not actually complaining of Moses he had a hard time preventing them from taking him for a god — for Him whom he preached.

10.

That was at bottom not so absurd. For what he now began to require of the poor creatures was beyond the powers of ordinary humanity. Indeed, it could hardly have occurred to the mind of a mere mortal. It made one gape. Directly after Miriam's song Moses forbade all further exultation over the destruction of Egypt. He announced that Jahwe's angelic hosts had been about to join in the song of triumph, when the Deity told them: "What, my creatures are sinking in the sea and you would sing?" Moses put about this brief but amazing tale. He added: "Thou shalt not rejoice at the fall of thy foe; the heart shall not be glad at his overthrow." It was the first time that the whole huddle of them, twelve thousand and some hundred head, including three thousand arms-bearing men, had been addressed like that as "thou" — a form that took them all in and at the same time fixed its eye on each one singly: man and wife, greybeard and infant. It deeply moved each one of them, as though a finger had touched each breast. Thou shalt not shout with joy at the fall of thy foe: that was in the highest degree unnatural. But obviously this unnaturalness was connected with the invisible nature of Moses' God who wanted to be their God. It began to dawn upon the more mentally alert among the dark-skinned herd just what all this meant, and how uncanny and irretrievable it was to have vowed allegiance to an invisible God.

They were in the land of Sinai; in fact, in the desert of Shur, a dismal tract which they would leave only to enter another as dismal, the desert of Paran. There was no reason why this desert should have two names. The two tracts abutted aridly one on the other and were one and the same waterless, cropless, accursed flatland, running up into dead hills; three days' march long, or even four and five. Moses had done well to begin his shaping task at the moment when his prestige was highest, at the Red Sea. For presently he was "this man Moses who led us out of Egypt" — that is to say, into misfortune. Loud grumbling assailed his ears. After three days the water supply dwindled. Thousands were thirsty — over their heads the relentless sun, under their feet the barren, flinty waste, whether it still called itself Shur or already Paran. "What shall we drink?" They shouted it aloud without feeling for the suffering of their responsible leader. He wished he might be the only one not to drink, never again to drink if only they could, if only he might not hear "Why have you made us leave Egypt?" To suffer alone is slight in comparison with having to pay for the sufferings of such a host. Moses was a much troubled man, and remained so — troubled above all men on earth.

And very soon there was no more to eat; for how long could their hastily snatched supply of unleavened cakes hold out? "What shall we eat?" This cry too arose with weeping and railing, and Moses had heavy hours alone with his God, when he told Him how harsh He was to lay the whole burden of this people upon Moses, His servant. "Did I then conceive and bear them all," he asked, "that you can say to me 'Carry them in your arms'? Where shall I get food for all the people? They weep before me and say 'Give us meat that we may eat.' I cannot carry so many alone, it is too hard for me. Then rather slay me that I behold not my misfortune and theirs."

But Jahwe did not leave him quite in the lurch. As for drink, on the fifth day they reached a table-land and, crossing it, found a spring with trees, called on the maps Marah, as Joshua knew. The water had a bad taste due to unpalatable minerals in it. Bitter disappointment followed and prolonged grumbling, until Moses, made inventive by necessity, contrived a sort of filter which largely did away with the bad taste. To his people it was a little miracle and turned railing into praise, greatly improving his reputation once more. The words "who brought us out of the land of Egypt" had again a mellow ring.

And as for the food, here too there came a miracle, which at first evoked joyous amaze. Wide stretches of the desert of Paran proved to be covered with an edible fungus, a sweet-tasting flake, small and round, that looked like coriander-seed and was very perishable, beginning to smell if not eaten at once. But grated or pounded and baked in flat cakes it made a tolerable food, tasting rather like wafers and honey, some thought; others found it rather like seed-cake made with oil.

That was the first, more favourable verdict. But it did not last. After a few days they got sick and tired of the manna. As their sole food it became repulsive to them, and they complained: "We remember all the fish we had in Egypt, the gourds and leeks and onions and garlic. Our souls are weary, for our eyes see naught but manna."

Moses heard and suffered. And heard, of course, the eternal question, Why have you made us leave Egypt? What he asked God was: What shall I do with this folk? They will eat no more manna. You will see, only a little more and they will stone me!

1.

From that fate at least he was more or less protected by young Joshua and the body of troops he had already gathered to his standard in Goshen. They surrounded the Liberator whenever grumbling and threats increased among the masses. They had been but a small body at first, and young, but Joshua only awaited a proper occasion to make himself commander-in-chief and put all the arms-bearing men, the whole three thousand, under his orders. And he was aware that such an occasion was at hand.

Moses was dependent on the young man, whom he had named with the name of God. There were times when he would have been lost without him. For Moses was a religious man, and his virility, sturdy and strong as it was, like that of a broad-wristed mason, was a spiritual virility, turned in upon itself, held in check by God, full of fanatic inward zeal, and in his preoccupation with holiness blind to outward appearances. He had a sort of flightiness in odd contrast to his habitual pose of brooding contemplation, with his mouth and beard covered by his hand. In all that he thought and did Moses had one single idea: that of getting his father's sect to himself that he might form it to his desire and carve out of this hapless, amorphous mass, which he so loved, the sacred image of the Deity. But he had thought little or nothing about the risks of freedom or the hardships of the desert or the trouble of getting such a horde as this through it in safety. He had not even much considered whither he would take them afterwards, nor had he at all prepared himself for the practical duties of leadership. So he could but be glad to have Joshua at his side; while for his part the youth worshipped Moses' religious fervour and put his own sturdy, forthright young manhood utterly at Moses' command.

It was due to Joshua that they moved in a straight line through the desert and did not go round in circles till they died. Joshua mapped their course by the stars, reckoned the daily march, and took care that they reached a water supply at tolerable, sometimes just barely tolerable, intervals. It was Joshua too who found out that the manna could be eaten. In a word he was a prop to the reputation of his master; and whenever the phrase "the man who led us out of Egypt" began to sound threatening he took steps to turn it into praise. He had the goal clear in his mind and steered thither direct, in agreement with Moses. For both of them felt that they needed an immediate goal, a settled even though not permanent habitation, a place where they could live and have time, quite a good deal of time: partly (this in Joshua's mind) that they might breed and produce the recruits for a larger body of troops; partly (this in Moses' view) that he might first mould this clay in God's likeness, might make something respectable and even pure and holy of it and dedicate the work of his hands to the invisible God, toward whom he yearned both in his soul and in his broad-wristed body.

The goal was the oasis of Kadesh. We have seen that the desert of Paran immediately adjoined the desert of Shur. But south of Paran lay still another, the desert of Sinai. Yet not quite so immediately, for at one point in between the two lay the oasis of Kadesh. It was a plain, beautiful by comparison with the desert — a green refreshment in the waterless waste, with three large springs and a number of smaller ones; a day's march long by half a march wide. It had good soil and was covered with fresh pasture. In short, it was an inviting stretch of land with ample food and game, large enough to lodge and feed a body like theirs.

Joshua knew of this attractive spot; it was well marked on the map he carried in his head. Moses knew about it too, but it was Joshua's idea that they should make for it. Here was his chance. A pearl like Kadesh did not, of course, lie there owner-less. It was occupied in strength; yet perhaps not too strongly, young Joshua hoped. Still, if they wanted it they must fight for it with those in possession — and that was Amalek.

It was some of the Amalekites who held Kadesh, and cer-tainly they would defend it. Joshua made it clear to Moses that there must be war, a battle between Jahwe and Amalek, even if permanent enmity were the result from generation to generation. They had to have the oasis; it was the perfect site for their com-bined needs of physical and spiritual growth.

Moses hesitated. For him one of the implications of the in-visible nature of God was that a man should not covet his neigh-bour's house, and he voiced the objection to his henchman. But Joshua answered: "Kadesh is not Amalek's house." For the youth was knowledgeable in time as well as in space, and he knew that historically Kadesh had been occupied — he did not indeed know when — by Hebrews, hence kinfolk, descendants of the fathers who had been driven out and scattered by the Amalekites. Kadesh, then, had been stolen, and it was fair enough to steal it back.

Moses doubted it. But he had his own grounds for thinking that Kadesh was a domain of Jahwe and belonged to those who were in a Covenant with Him. Kadesh meant "sanctuary," and the oasis was so called not alone on account of its natural ad-vantages. In a sense it was a shrine of the Midianite Jahwe, whom Moses had confessed as the God of his Fathers. Not far off, east-wards toward Edom, lay in a line with other mountains Mount Horeb, which Moses had visited from Midian and on whose slope God had revealed Himself in the burning bush. Horeb, the mountain, was Jahwe's seat — one of them, at least. His origi-nal seat, Moses knew, was Mount Sinai, in the range to the far south. But between Sinai and Horeb, the site of Moses' commis-sion, there was close connection, in that Jahwe had His seat on both of them; you could put them on a par, you could call Horeb Sinai. And Kadesh was called what it was, a sanctuary, because, roughly speaking, it lay at the foot of the sacred mount.

Moses, then, accepted Joshua's plan and instructed him to prepare for the armed encounter between Jahwe and Amalek.

12. The battle took place; that is historic fact. It was a hard-fought battle, swaying to and fro. But Israel issued from it triumphant. This name, Israel, meaning "God fighteth," had been conferred by Moses on his people to strengthen them for the ordeal. He explained that it was a very old name, long forgotten: Jacob the patriarch had wrested it by struggle for himself and given it to his people. It did the tribes a great deal of good. The loose unorganized mass, being now all Israel, fought unitedly and well under the aegis of this name, ranged in order of battle and commanded by Joshua the youthful general and Caleb his second in command.

When the Amalekites beheld the approaching hosts they did not doubt the meaning of what they saw. Such a sight has but one meaning. They did not remain in the oasis and await the attack, but issued forth at once in great strength into the wilderness. They were more numerous and better armed than the Israelites, and the battle was joined between the two armies amid whirling clouds of dust, loud battle-cries, and great tumult and din. It was still more unequal because Joshua's people were plagued with thirst and for some days had had only manna to eat. On the other hand, they were strong in their leaders, the clear-eyed youth Joshua and Moses the man of God.

Moses, indeed, at the beginning of the fray, had withdrawn, together with his half-brother Aaron and Miriam the prophetess, upon a hill whence they could look down on the place of decision. His virility was not of the martial kind, but rather of a priestly nature; hence it was his vocation, unquestioned by any, to call upon God with uplifted arms and in words of fire — as for instance, "Rise up, Jahwe of the myriads, the thousands of

Israel, and smite the foe, that they who hate Thee may flee and be scattered from before Thy face!"

They fled not and they scattered not, or they did so at first only locally and temporarily. For though Israel raged mightily, mad with thirst and disgust of manna, yet the myriads of Amalek were more, and after briefly falling back they again advanced, and even got dangerously close to Moses' own hill. But it turned out that as long as Moses held up his arms to heaven, Israel triumphed; but if he let them fall, then Amalek did. Of course, he could not hold them up all the time; so Aaron and Miriam supported him under the arm-pits and held his arms aloft. But what that meant one can measure by the fact that the battle lasted from morn to eve, and in all that time Moses had to sustain his painful attitude. So we see what a hard time spiritual virility had up there praying on its hill — very likely even harder than sturdy youth hacking away down in the melée.

Even so, Moses could not keep it up all day on end. His assistants had to let the master's arms down for a minute once in a while; and straightway Jahwe's men lost blood and ground. Then they hoisted the arms up again, and those below drew fresh strength from the sight. Joshua's military talents also availed to bring about the favourable issue of the conflict. He had a real gift both for planned strategy and for brilliant inspiration, and invented novel manœuvres, quite unheard of before, at least in the wilderness; besides he had a strength of purpose that could look on undismayed at a temporary loss of ground. He assembled the best troops he had, a selected group — the avenging angels, in short — on the enemy's right wing, exerted great pressure there, forced it to fall back, and scored a local victory, though elsewhere the greater strength of Amalek was in the ascendant and gaining ground from Israel in violent lunges. However, by breaking through on the flank Joshua got into Amalek's rear, so that the latter had to turn around and fight him while still engaged with the main body of Israel's army, which had been close to surrender but now took heart afresh. Now Amalek lost his head; panic seized on him, and he gave up the fight. "Treason! Despair!" he cried. "All is lost! Jahwe is over us, a

God of insatiable cruelty!" And with this despairing cry Amalek let fall his sword and was slain.

Only a few of his party succeeded in fleeing northwards and joining the main group of their tribe. But Israel entered into the oasis of Kadesh, which proved to have a broad, swift stream running through it and to be planted with fruit-trees and nut-bushes and filled with bees, song-birds, quail and hares. Some of the children of Amalek had remained behind; these swelled the numbers of Israel's progeny, while Amalek's wives became the wives and servants of the Israelites.

13.

Moses, though his arms were stiff long afterwards, was a happy man. That he remained a much troubled one, tried above any other on earth, we shall soon see. But in the beginning he was very happy over the way things had turned out. The exodus had been accomplished, Pharaoh's avenging might was sunk in the reedy sea, the journey through the wilderness had gone off well and with Jahwe's help the battle of Kadesh was won. And now he stood before his father's people and was "the man Moses who has led us out of Egypt." He had needed just this success in order to begin his work, the work of purification and shaping in the sign of the Invisible; the work of chipping and chiselling at this flesh and blood, after which his soul had yearned. Happy he was to have this flesh now by itself in the open, in the oasis whose name meant sanctuary. Here was his workshop.

He showed the people the mountain visible among others at the back side of the desert east of Kadesh: Horeb, which one might also call Sinai. It was covered with bushes two-thirds of the way up, above that bare; and it was Jahwe's seat. The statement was not hard to credit; for it looked unusual, being distinguished from the others by a cloud that never went away, but lay at all times like a thatch on its head. In the daytime it looked grey, but at night it was lighted up. There, so his people heard, on the thicketed slope below the rocky peak, Jahwe had spoken to Moses out of the burning bush and commanded him to lead them out of Egypt. They listened with fear and trembling, which with them still took the place of awe and worship. Actually all of them, even the bearded men, trembled at the knees like savages and cowards when Moses pointed out the mountain in its abiding cap of cloud and told them the God sat there who had a mind to them and would be their only God. Moses, his fists shaking, scolded them for their pusillanimity and laid himself out to give them a better and more familiar attitude towards Jahwe by setting up a shrine for Him in the midst of them, at Kadesh itself.

For Jahwe, it seemed, had a movable presence; that, like so much else, fell together with His invisibility. He sat on Sinai, He sat on Horeb, and now Moses — directly they had got settled into the houses of the Amalekites at Kadesh — made Him a dwelling in their very midst, near Moses' own, which he called the tent of meeting or assembly, also the tabernacle, where were kept certain sacred articles which could be used about the Imageless and in His honour. They were chiefly things that Moses remembered as having to do with the cult of the Midianite Jahwe. First there was a sort of chest with carrying-poles, on which, according to Moses (and certainly he ought to know) the God sat throned invisible and would be borne thus into the field and in the front of the battle if ever Amalek should return seeking revenge. A bronze staff with a serpent's head, in short the so-called brazen serpent, was kept beside the chest in memory of Aaron's well-intentioned trick before Pharaoh. It had now the added meaning that it might also stand for the staff that Moses had stretched out over the reedy shallows to divide the waters. Likewise the "Ephod" was kept in the Jahwe tent: a sort of bag for the drawing of lots, the "Urim and Thummim," the yes or no, right or wrong, which was appealed to in cases of difficulties and disagreement, to invoke Jahwe's judgement where man's failed.

But in most cases Moses did the judging himself. Indeed, almost the first thing he did at Kadesh was to set up a judgement seat, where on certain days he resolved disputes and gave out law, sitting beside the largest spring in the oasis, the Me-Meribah or water of judgement, already so called. Thence flowed the law, even as the water flowed out of the earth. But when one remembers that there were all together some twelve thousand five hundred souls who applied to him for justice, one can measure the extent of Moses' tribulations. For they pressed about his seat at the fountain, the more so that the idea of "right" was something quite new to this lost, bewildered sect. Indeed, they scarce knew there was such a thing — and now they came to hear that the "right" was immediately associated with the invisibility of their God and His holiness, that it was under His direct protection. Further, they heard that in this new idea of right was included the idea of "wrong." And this the masses for a long time utterly failed to grasp. They thought that where the right flowed everyone must get his rights; they would not and could not believe that a man was getting his "rights" even when he was judged in the wrong and had to go away with his nose out of joint. Such a man, of course, cursed himself for not having settled the quarrel with his opponent in the natural way, with a stone, when the result might have been quite different. Only slowly did they learn from Moses that such ideas were not in harmony with the invisibility of God, and that nobody got his nose put out of joint who was judged unright by the law, for that the law was always both beautiful and austere in its holy invisibility, no matter whether it pronounced a man in the right or in the wrong.

So Moses had not alone to pronounce the law, but also to teach it, and was troubled indeed. He had studied it in his school in Thebes, the Egyptian legal rolls and the Codes of Hammurabi, the King on the Euphrates. That helped him to clear judgement in many of the cases that came up. For instance, if an ox had gored a man or a woman the ox should be stoned and his flesh not eaten, but the owner of the ox was innocent unless it was well known that the ox was used to push with his horns and the owner had not kept him in. In that case the owner too lost his life, unless he could redeem it with thirty silver shekels. Or if any man opened a pit and did not cover it properly, so that an ox or an ass fell in, then the owner of the pit must make it good by giving money to him, and the dead beast should be his. Or whatever happened of bodily injury, harm to slaves, breaking in and stealing, damage to fields, arson or abuse of trust; in all such cases and in a hundred others Moses found judgement, leaning on Hammurabi, and pronounced between right and wrong. But there were too many cases for one judge, and the seat by the fount of judgement was overrun. If the master investigated thoroughly one single case, he never got done, he had to postpone judgement, fresh cases came up; he was plagued over and above the lot of mankind.

14. So it was very good that his brother-in-law Jethro, from Midian, visited him at Kadesh and gave him a piece of advice, an idea that his own obstinate conscience would never have hit upon. Soon after he arrived in the oasis Moses had sent down to Midian to his father-in-law to have him send back his wife Zipporah and his two sons, for he had given them into his charge during the tribulations in Egypt. But Jethro was kind enough to come in person to hand over Moses' wife and sons, to embrace him and hear how things were going.

He was a portly sheik with a merry eye and easy gestures, a man of the world, prince of a developed and socially experienced people. He was welcomed with due ceremony and went in to Moses into his hut and heard, not without amazement, how one of his gods, the very one who was invisible amongst them, had conducted Himself so surprisingly towards Moses and his people and how He had known how to deliver them out of the hands of the Egyptians.

"Who would have thought it?" he said. "He is obviously

much greater than we supposed, and what you tell me makes me afraid that we have been negligent in His service up till now. I must see to it that He receives greater honour amongst us." The next day public burnt offerings were appointed, such as Moses seldom commanded. He had no exaggerated ideas about offerings; they were not essential, he thought, before the Invisible; it was a custom practised by other peoples, the peoples of the world. Whereas Jahwe had said: "Above all hearken to My voice; that is, to the voice of My servant Moses. For then I will be your God and you My people." But this time there were slayings and burnings for Jahwe's nostrils as well as in celebration of Jethro's visit. And on the next day early in the morning he took his brother-in-law with him to the judgement fount to be present at a sitting and see how Moses sat and judged the people. They clustered round him from morn to eve, and there was no end to it.

"Tell me, my dear brother-in-law," said the guest as they left the place together, "tell me, why on earth you give yourself all that trouble! Sitting alone and all the crowd standing round from morn to eve! Why do it?"

"I must do so," Moses answered. "The people come to me that I may judge between each one and his neighbour and show him God's justice and His laws."

"But, my dear fellow, how can you be so impracticable?" said Jethro again. "Is that a way to govern? Does a ruler let himself be skinned alive, doing everything himself? You are getting so worn out it is a shame; you can hardly see out of your eyes, you lose your voice — and your people are just as tired out as you are. That is no way to do it; you can't go on doing everything yourself, and it is not at all necessary. Just listen to me! If you represent God to the people and bring the most important things to His attention yourself — things which are of general concern — that is quite enough. Look round," he said with an easy wave of the hand, "among your people for upright and judicious men, a bit looked up to, and set them over the people to be rulers over a thousand, over a hundred, yes, over fifty and ten, and have them judge according to justice and the law you have given to the people. And only in a great matter shall they bring it to you, settling the lesser ones themselves. You don't need to know anything about it. That is the way we do, and it will greatly ease matters for you. I should not have had my fine little paunch, nor could I have got away to visit you, if I thought I had to know everything and do the way you do."

"But the judges will take presents," answered Moses gloomily, "and give the judgement to the godless. For presents make the seeing blind and wrench the true cause the false way."

"Yes, I know," responded Jethro. "Well I know. But you will have to stand a little of that sort of thing so long as justice more or less prevails and there is law and order, even if it gets a bit complicated with presents and such. You see, the ones that take presents are ordinary people; but after all, the people are just ordinary too. So for the ordinary it has meaning and is suited and agreeable to the community. Besides, if some man has his business judged ill by the judge over ten because the judge has taken presents from the unrighteous, then let him follow the usual routine and course of justice and appeal to the judge over fifty, and then over an hundred, and finally over a thousand. He gets the most presents of all, so he has a more open mind and the petitioner will get justice from him — if he has not got tired of the whole thing first."

Thus Jethro, with such soothing voice and gesture that it made life easier only to look at him; it was clear that he was priest-king of a developed and civilized desert folk. Moses listened pensively and nodded his head. He had the suggestible soul of the lonely, spiritual-minded man, who nods musingly at the wisdom of the world and perceives that it may well be right. And he did indeed take the advice of his experienced brother-in-law — there was really nothing else for him to do. He appointed lay judges to sit by the fountain and dispense petty justice, guided by his instructions. These men judged the ordinary day-to-day cases (as when an ass fell into a pit), and only the capital cases came up to him, the priest of God. The most important of all were decided by the sacred lots.

So now he was no longer involved beyond reason, but got his hands free for the educational program he proposed to carry out on the unformed mass of this folk, the theatre for which had been fought for and won by the strategic-minded young Joshua, that is to say, the oasis of Kadesh. No doubt Justice was an important factor among all the implications of the Invisible; but, after all, it was only one — and how many factors there were! And what a task it was, how long and arduous, demanding both great patience and great fury! It would be hard enough to turn this uncivilized, ill-mannered horde into a decent ordinary folk fitting into the ordinary decent ways of life. That would be one thing; but quite another to make something extraordinary of them, a set apart and sanctified people, a purified community with its eyes fixed upon the Invisible and addressed to Him alone.

15. The kindred soon saw what it meant to have fallen into the hands of a man like Moses, a man of wrath and of infinite patience, a workman responsible alone for the invisible God. They saw that it had been only the beginning, that unnatural command to refrain from shouting for joy when the foe was drowned. In fact, even that beginning was premature. For it demanded of them an advanced stage of enlightenment resting on many premises of which they were ignorant. They had a long, long way to go before they could find it anything but utterly inhuman. They were, in short, nothing but raw material, flesh and blood, and the fundamental conceptions of purity and holiness entirely escaped them. So much is clear from the way Moses had to go to work from the very beginning and the pathetically primitive laws he had to instil into them. They did not like it: the block is not on the mason's side, but against him, and the first thing that happens in its shaping seems the most unnatural of all.

Moses was always among them, now here and now there, in

this settlement and that; stocky, with flat nose and wide-set eyes. He shook his fists on their broad wrists; he nagged and nudged, he pushed and shoved, he bounced and bossed and rubbed and scrubbed at them, and always the invisibility of God was his text — Jahwe's, who had led them out of Egypt in order to make them His people, and who must have holy folk about him even as He Himself was holy. At the moment they were nothing but an unlicked crew, and they relieved themselves just wherever they happened to be. That was a shame and a nuisance. You must have a place outside, for you to go out to when you have need. And you must keep a little trowel by you and dig a little hole before you sit down and afterwards you must cover it up. For in your dwelling the Lord your God moves about, and so it must be a pure and holy place so that He does not hold His nose and turn away. For godliness begins with cleanliness, and if there is purity even in the lowest things, then that is the lowly beginning of all purity. Do you understand that, Ahiman, and you, Naemi, his woman? Next time let me see everybody with a trowel, or the avenging angel will be after you!

Furthermore, you must be clean and bathe a great deal in running water for your health's sake; for without health there is no purity or holiness, and sickness is unclean. If you think that filth is healthier than cleanliness, then you are a fool, and you will be stricken with jaundice, fig-boils, and the boils of Egypt. If you practise not cleanliness, then an evil black pox will break out and the seeds of pestilence go from blood to blood. Learn to distinguish between purity and impurity, or you cannot stand before the Invisible and are simply the scum of the earth. If a man or woman have a consuming eruption, an evil issue on the body, scab or itch, he or she shall be impure and not suffered in the dwelling-place, but be put outside it, set apart in uncleanness, even as the Lord has set you apart to be pure. And whatever such a one has touched or lain upon, and the saddle he rode on, shall be burned. But if he become clean while set apart, he shall reckon seven days to see if he be verily clean, and bathe thoroughly with water; then he may come back.

38.

Distinguish, I say to you, and be delicate in the sight of God or you cannot be holy as I would have you be. You eat everything regardless, without discrimination or shame, and it is an abomination to you. For you should eat one thing and not another, and feel both pride and disgust. Whatsoever parteth the hoof among the beasts and cheweth the cud, that shall ye eat. But what cheweth the cud and hath hoofs but divides them not, as the camel, it is unclean to you and you shall not eat it. Note that the good camel is not unclean, for he is God's creature; but he is not proper as food — as little as the swine, which likewise you shall not eat, for though it part the hoof, yet it does not chew the cud. So make a distinction! All that has fins and scales in the water may ye eat, but all that glides about without them, the tribe of newts, that is indeed from God too, but as food shall be an abomination to you. And among the fowls these are they you shall hold in abhorrence: the eagle, the hawk, the osprey, the vulture, and after their kind; every raven after his kind, the ostrich, the night-owl, the cuckoo, the little owl, the swan, the great owl, the bat, the bittern, the stork, the heron, the crane, as well as the swallow. I forgot the hoopoe; that also shall you avoid. Who will eat the weasel, the mouse, the toad, or the hedgehog? Who is so low as to eat the lizard, the mole, or the blindworm, or anything that creeps upon the earth or crawls upon his belly? But you do it, and thereby make your souls an abomination. If ever again I see anyone eat a blindworm, I will see to it he does not do so again. Truly he will not die of it, nor is it harmful; but it is shameful, and much shall be shameful to you. So shall you eat no carrion; that is harmful, too.

So he made diet rules for them and restricted them in their eating — but not only therein. For he did the same in matters of love and lust; for here too they were very promiscuous, and their ways were vulgar in the extreme. You shall not break the bed vow, he told them, for it is a sacred bar. But do you know what it means, not to break the bed vow? It means an hundred restrictions, with respect to the holiness of God; and not alone that you shall not covet your neighbour's wife, for that is the least of it. You live in the flesh, but are vowed to the Invisible, and marriage is the whole content of all purity in the flesh before God's countenance. Therefore you shall not take a woman and her mother — to give you an example — for that is not fitting. And you must never lie with your sister to see her shame and she yours, for that is incest. Nor shall you even lie with your aunt, for it is worthy neither of her nor of you, and you should shrink from it. When a woman has her sickness you shall avoid her and not approach the source of her blood. But if a man has a shameful issue in his sleep, he shall be impure until the next evening and shall bathe thoroughly with water.

I hear you offer your daughter for a whore and take money from her? Do not so, for if you persist I will have you stoned. And what are you thinking of, to sleep with a boy as with a woman? That is abnormal and an abomination among the people, and both shall die the death. But if one do so with beasts, whether man or woman, they shall be rooted out and shall be strangled together with the beast.

Imagine their consternation at all these restrictions! At first they had the feeling that if one obeyed at all, life would not be worth living. For Moses sprang about among them with his little chisel, making the chips fly. Even literally: that about the punishments and prohibitions proved to be no joke at all, for behind them stood young Joshua and the avenging angels.

"I am the Lord your God," he said to them — and ran the risk of having them take him at his word — "who led you out of the land of Egypt and set you apart from all people. Therefore you shall also separate the pure from the impure and not go whoring after other peoples, but be sacred to Me alone. For I the Lord am holy and I have set you apart to be Mine. The greatest uncleanness of all is to trouble about any other God save Me, for I am a jealous God. The worst of all is to make an image, let it look like man or woman, ox or sparrow-hawk, fish or worm, for therewith you have already fallen away from Me, even though the image should be of Me. Such a one might just as well sleep with his sister or with a beast, for there is no great difference, and one thing leads to the other. So take care, for I am among you and I see all. He who whores after the dead gods of Egypt, to him will I come home! I will hunt him into the desert and cut him off like an outcast. In the same way whosoever sacrifices to Moloch, of whom, I well know, you still are mindful, and is smitten with his power, such a one is evil, and evilly will I requite him. Therefore you shall not have your son or your daughter go through fire after the foolish old custom, nor shall you mark the flight and cries of birds, nor mumble with soothsayers, augurs, and interpreters of signs, nor question the dead nor meddle in magic in My name. If a man be a villain and bring in My name to witness in his mouth, that shall avail him least of all, for him will I consume. But also to scratch or cut the face or shear the brows or mar the countenance in mourning for the dead, that is but cheap magic and an abomination. I will not have it."

How great was their consternation! So now they might not even mourn by making little cuts on the face; not even the least little bit of tattooing. So this was what it meant to have an invisible God! To covenant, they perceived, was to be limited extremely. Behind Moses' every prohibition stood the avenging angel; and since the people did not want to be driven into the desert, all the things that Moses forbade came to seem frightful to them. At first this was so only in connection with the punishment; but after a while the thing itself came to be thought of as an evil. And when a man broke the law it made him feel sick, even without thinking of the punishment.

Bridle your heart, so he told them, and cast not your eyes on another's goods to covet them, for that may easily lead to taking them, either by stealth, which is cowardly, or by murder, which is barbarous. Jahwe and I would have you neither cowards nor barbarians; the mean between them is what you must be — in other words, decent. Have you understood this much? Stealing is a skulking sin; but murder — whether out of rage or greed or greedy rage or raging greed — murder is a deed that cries to heaven. He who commits it, against him will I set My face, that he know not where he may hide himself. For he has shed blood, and, after all, blood is a great mystery, sacred and held in awe — an altar-gift to Me and an atonement. Blood shall you not eat, and no flesh when blood is in it, for it is Mine. Now whosoever is smeared with man's blood, his heart shall shrink with cold horror, and I will hunt him until he runs from himself to the end of the earth. Say Amen!

And they all said Amen, hoping that when Moses used the word "murder" he meant literally killing, to which they had no great mind — or at least not often. But it turned out that Jahwe gave the word a meaning as broad as that which he had given to the breaking of the marriage vow. He meant by it all sorts of things, until murder and manslaughter ended by beginning with every injury one man did to another. Blood flowed, it appeared, in every overreaching or taking advantage — and to such nearly everybody had a mind. They must not deal falsely with each other, not bear false witness; they must give honest measure, full-weight pounds and bushels. It was all most unnatural; and for quite a while their natural fear of punishment was the only feature that seemed human at all.

A man must honour his father and his mother. Moses enjoined it upon them. But even this had a broader meaning than one would have supposed. Whoso lifted his hand against his begetter and cursed him — well, yes, such a one ought to be done away. But when the honouring extended to those who only might have been his father — ? You must stand in the presence of grey hairs, cross your arms, and bow your simple head, you understand? Respect to God will have it so. The only consolation was that since your neighbour was forbidden to kill you, you had the prospect of getting old and grey yourself, so that the others would have to stand up and bow.

It came in the end to this: that age was a figure of speech for the old in general, for everything that was not of today or yesterday, but came from afar; for the pious and traditional, the usage of the fathers. To that one must pay honour and reverence. So shall you celebrate the day when I led you out of Egypt, the day of the unleavened bread, and always the day when I rested from the Creation. My day, the Sabbath, shall you not defile with the sweat of your brow; I forbid you. For I have led you out of the Egyptian house of bondage with mighty hand

and outstretched arm, where you were a servant and a beast of burden, and My day shall be the day of your deliverance; that shall you celebrate. Six days shall you be an husbandman or a maker of ploughs, a potter or coppersmith, a cabinet-maker; but on My day shall ye put on fresh garments and be nothing but a man and open your eyes to the Invisible.

You were a slave there in Egypt, spent with toil — be mindful of it in your dealings with your own servants! You were a stranger among the children of Egypt — remember it in your treatment of the stranger among you, for instance, the children of Amalek whom God gave into your hands, and do not abuse them. Look on them as yourself and give them even-handed justice, or I will interfere, for they stand under Jahwe's shield. Make no such absurd and arrogant distinction between you and another man as to think that you alone are real and essential, while he is only a simulacrum. You have dear life in common, and it is only chance you are not he. Therefore love not yourself alone, but him as well, and do with him as you would he would do with you in his place. Be pleasant with each other and kiss the finger-tips as you pass and bow politely and greet him, saying, I hope I see you well! For it is just as important that he is well as that you are. And if it be only out of mannerliness that you do so, and kiss your finger-tips, yet after all the mere gesture must plant in your heart some feeling of the kind you should cherish for your neighbour. — Say Amen to all that!

16. But saying Amen did not get them very far. They only said it because he was the man who with luck had led them out of Egypt, sunk Pharaoh's waggons in the sea, and won the battle of Kadesh. It took a long time for his teachings and injunctions, his restrictions, commands, and prohibitions, to get under their skins or even to seem to do so. It was a big job he had undertaken: to raise up to the Lord out of these hordes a sanctified group, a cleansed community. In the sweat of his brow he worked on his mission, there in Kadesh his workshop. His wide-set eyes were everywhere. He chiselled, blasted, planed, and smoothed at the rebellious block with sturdy patience, with repeated forbearance, often forgiving, sometimes blazing with scorn and lashing out ruthlessly. Even so he often despaired when this flesh on which he laboured continued so wilful, so forgetful, so unregenerate; when the people failed to use their little trowels or slept with their sisters or with the cow or ate blindworms or mutilated their faces, sat mumbling with sooth-sayers, committed petty thieveries, or even slew each other. "O beasts!" he said to them then, "you will see, the Lord will come down on you suddenly and blot you out." But to the Lord Him-self he said: "What shall I do with this flesh, and why hast Thou removed Thy favour from me to lay upon my shoulders what I cannot bear? Rather will I clean the dung from a stall which seven years long has seen neither water nor spade, or clear a jungle with my hands to make a ploughed field, than try to make a God-fearing people out of this filth. How do I come to be car-rying this folk in my arms as if I had borne them? I am only half kin to them, on my father's side. So, I beseech You, make me glad of my life and let me off this task, for rather will I stran-gle myself!"

But God answered him out of his inmost self with so plain a voice that he heard it with his ears, and he fell on his face:

"Just because you are only half their kin, from the side of him buried, are you the man to work upon them for me and raise them up to me a seemly folk. For if you were in their very hearts and entirely one of them, you would not see them as they are and could not lay hand to them. But anyhow this lament of yours and your trying to beg off — all that is only pretence. For you surely see that a beginning has already been made with them; already you have made them a conscience, so that they are uncomfortable when they do wrong. So do not pretend to me that you have not the greatest zeal to your task. It is My zeal you have, godly zeal, and without it your life would turn to disgust, as the manna to the people even after a few days. Of course, if I were to strangle you, then you could do without it; but no other way."

Moses, despite his misgivings, could see all that; he nodded at Jahwe's words as he lay on his face, and then again he stood up to his vow. But he was a man of grief, and that not only in his chosen task. For trouble and vexation reached into his family life; there was annoyance and envy and discord. It came through his own fault, if you like, for his senses were the cause of the affliction. The work left them raw and craving, and he fixed his heart on an Ethiopian; yes, the notorious Ethiopian female. For we know that at that time he lived with this woman, in addition to his first wife Zipporah, the mother of his sons. She was a person from the land of Kush, who had come as a child to Egypt, lived among the tribes in Goshen, and joined the exodus. No doubt she had already known more than one man; and still Moses took her to his bed. In her way she was a splendid piece of flesh, with towering breasts and rolling whites to her eyes; she had pouting lips, wherein to sink in a kiss might be an adventure to any man, and her skin smelled of spicery. Moses clung to her for her power to relax him, and could not part from her although he faced the hostility of his own family on her account: not only of his Midianitic wife and sons, but even more of his half-brother and sister, Miriam and Aaron. Zipporah indeed, having much of her brother Jethro's cosmopolitan poise, got on tolerably with her rival, especially as the woman took pains to hide her feminine triumph and behaved obsequiously towards the true wife. As for Zipporah, she treated the Ethiopian with more mockery than anger; and even to Moses himself she bridled her jealousy and behaved in the same spirit. The sons, Gershom and Eliezer, who were soldiers in Joshua's army, possessed too much feeling for discipline to contend against their father, though they did show some anger and chagrin over his behaviour.

But things were different with Miriam and Aaron, the sanctimonious. Their hatred for the black woman was more venomous than the others' because it was by way of being an outlet for the deeper and more general anger that united them against Moses. Some time earlier they had begun to be jealous of his close relation to God, his spiritual leadership, his personal election, which they considered in great part imaginary. They thought they were just as good as he was, or better; saying to each other: "Does the Lord then speak by Moses only; speaks he not also by us? Who is this man Moses, that he should have raised himself so far above others?" Such emotions lay at the bottom of the offence they took at his relations with the black woman, and always when they attacked their brother and bitingly reproached him on account of his passionate nights, he knew to his sorrow that it was only the occasion for their real grievance; very soon they would go on to the injustice done them by his elevation.

One day they were with him in his house at sunset, tormenting him as usual with the black woman here and the black woman there, and how he clung to her black breasts, and what a scandal it was and what a slap in Zipporah's face, his first wife, and what an unmasking of himself, who claimed to be a spiritual lord and Jahwe's unique representative on earth. And so on.

"Claim?" said he. "What God has laid upon me to be, that I am. But how hateful of you, how really very hateful, to grudge me my pleasure and the relaxation I get on the breast of my Ethiopian girl! For it is no sin before God, and there is no prohibition among all those which he gave me, against lying with an Ethiopian. Not that I know of."

Oh, yes, they said. He made arbitrary rules and prohibitions, and it would not surprise them to hear that it was explicitly commanded to lie with Ethiopians, he being in his own eyes the only mouthpiece Jahwe had. But they, Miriam and Aaron, were genuine children of Amram, grandson of Levi, whereas he was, after all, only a foundling from the reeds and ought to learn a little humility. For his obstinacy about the Ethiopian, quite aside from the shame of it, was shocking because it sprang from his arrogance and conceit.

"Who can help his vocation?" said he. "And who can help it if he chance to see a burning bush? Miriam, I have always esteemed your prophetic gifts and never disputed your power with the timbrel."

"Then why did you forbid my song 'Horse and Rider'?" she asked, "and refuse to let me play before the women in dances because, forsooth, God had forbidden His hosts to rejoice at the destruction of Egypt? That was hateful of you."

"And you, Aaron," went on the hard-pressed man, "you I made high priest of the tabernacle and gave into your keeping the ark, the ephod, and the brazen serpent. So highly do I esteem you."

"It was the least you could do," responded Aaron, "for without my eloquence you would never have won over the people to Jahwe with your stammering tongue, nor have moved them to embark on the exodus. Yet you call yourself the man who brought us out of Egypt. Now if you do esteem us and do not in your vanity exalt yourself above the genuine brother and sister, why not listen to our words and open your ears to our warning that you bring our whole seed into danger with your black philanderings? For it is a bitter draught for Zipporah, your Midianitic wife, and you offend all Midian thereby, so that Jethro, your brother-in-law, will yet fall upon us, all on account of that black fancy of yours."

"Jethro," said Moses with great self-control, "is a well-balanced man of the world, who would, of course, understand that Zipporah, with all due respect to her name, can no longer afford a highly troubled and burdened man like me the needful relaxation. But the skin of my Ethiopian is like cinnamon and oil of carnation in my nostrils, and therefore I implore you, dear friends, grant her to me!"

But that they would not. They railed and demanded that not only should he part from the Ethiopian and she should void his bed, but that he should send her out without water into the desert.

Then Moses' angry vein began to swell, his fists to shake along his thighs. But before he could open his mouth in reply there came quite another shaking. For Jahwe intervened. He set His face against the hard-hearted brother and sister and took the side of his servant Moses, so that they never forgot it. Something frightful and unprecedented came to pass.

7. The foundations shook; the earth quaked and leaped and reeled under their feet so that they could not stand, but all three staggered to and fro in the hut, whose columns were shaken as by giant hands. The firm earth swayed, not only to one side, but to all sides at once, in a dizzying and confounding way, so that their sensations were horrible. And added to this came a subterranean bellowing and banging and, from above and without, a braying as of the loudest trumpets, accompanied by other groanings and thunderings and crashings. It is peculiarly confounding, when you are about to explode with wrath, to have the Lord take it right out of your mouth and do it Himself — only far more mightily than you could have done, shaking the whole earth whereas you could only have shaken your fists.

Moses was less alarmed than the others, being at all times steadfast in his God. But Aaron and Miriam were pallid with fright; and all three of them rushed out of the hut and saw that the earth had opened its mouth in a great crack just in front of them, which had obviously been intended for Miriam and Aaron, and they had escaped only by a few ells from being swallowed up. And lo, the mountain to the east, back in the desert — Horeb or Sinai: what was happening to Horeb, and what going on with Mount Sinai? It stood there wrapped in flame and smoke, flinging glowing fragments to heaven in a distant crash of explosions, while fiery rivers ran down its sides. Thick smoke, with lightnings within, darkened the stars above the desert, and a rain of ashes began to fall on the oasis Kadesh.

Aaron and Miriam fell on their foreheads, for the crack so

clearly meant for them had terrified them sore, and the revelation of Jahwe on the mountain admonished them that they had gone too far and spoken as fools. Aaron cried out to Moses:

"Oh, my lord, this woman, my sister, has spoken foolishly and wantonly. Yet accept my plea and let the sin not rest upon her head that she has sinned against the Lord's anointed."

And Miriam too cried out and said: "My lord, no one could speak and utter more folly than my brother Aaron. Yet forgive him and let the sin not rest upon him, that God may not swallow him up because he taunted you with your Ethiopian."

Moses was not quite sure whether Jahwe's demonstration had really been addressed to his brother and sister on account of their hardness of heart, or whether it so came about that He just then summoned him to a council about the people and the work of education — for Moses was always expecting such a summons. He left it, however, as they had taken it, and replied:

"You see. But courage, children of Amram! I will speak a good word for you up there with God on the mount whither He summons me. For now shall you see, and all the people shall see, whether your brother is weakened by his black fancy or whether godly courage dwells in his heart as in no other. Upon the fiery mount I will go, alone, aloft to God, that I may hear His thoughts and fearless hold converse with the Frightful One, with thou and thou, far from men but upon their affairs. For long have I known that everything I have taught them to their salvation before Him the Holy One, He will collect together and sum up for all time, that I may bring it down to you from His mount and the people may possess it in the tabernacle together with the ark, the ephod, and the brazen serpent. Farewell! I may perish in God's tumult and in the fires of the mountain. That may well be; I must reckon with it. But if I return, I will bring you from His thunderings the final summing-up, the law of God."

Such indeed was his firm resolve, let the result be life or death. If he were ever to succeed in welding these froward, backsliding tribes into a God-fearing community observing the divine law, nothing could be more effective to that end than that

he should commit himself alone and unarmed unto Jahwe's ter-
rors and bring down thence the decalogue. Then, he thought,
they would be bound to keep it. They were running up now to
his dwelling from all sides, their knees shaking in terror of the
sign and the rendings and swayings of the earth, now dying
away in fainter tremors. And he rebuked them for their uncivilized terror and recommended propriety and composure. God,
he said, was summoning him on their account; he would go up
to Jahwe upon the mountain and by God's will bring them
something back. For their part, they should all go home and
prepare for an excursion. They should dedicate themselves, and
wash their clothes and themselves, and refrain from their wives;
for on the morrow they were all to go out from Kadesh into the
wilderness nearer to the mountain, and set up camp opposite it
and wait for him there, until he came back from his frightful
rendezvous and perhaps brought something to them.

So it came about, or more or less like that; for Moses, natu-
rally, had thought only of their washing their clothes and re-
fraining from their wives. But Joshua-ben-Nun the youthful
strategist considered what else was requisite for such a mass excursion; and he and his troops took care for the needful to be
taken along, water and food for thousands in the desert. He ar-
ranged for a service connecting Kadesh with the camp between
it and the mountain. He left Caleb, his lieutenant, and a detach-
ment of police in Kadesh with all those who could not or
would not go out. But the rest, when the third day had come and
all the preparations had been made, went out with carts and
cattle, one day's journey and a half towards the mountain. And
there Joshua made them an enclosure, still at a measurable dis-
tance from Jahwe's smouldering seat, and in Moses' name
strictly forbade them to climb the mountain or even to touch
its foot; for to the leader alone it was reserved to go so near to
God. Besides, it was dangerous; and whosoever approached the
mountain should be stoned or shot with bow and arrow. They
listened unconcerned, for such a rabble has not much itch to get
nearer to God, and to an ordinary man the mountain looked not
at all inviting. Not by day, when Jahwe stood upon it in a thick

cloud shot through with lightnings, and not by night, when the cloud glowed fierily and the whole peak as well.

Joshua was uncommonly proud of the godly intrepidity of his master, who on the very first day set out for the sacred mount on foot, before all the people. He held the pilgrim's staff and was provided only with an earthen flask, a few pieces of bread, and some tools — a hoe, a spade, a chisel, and a graving tool. Very proud was young Joshua of him and happy over the impression such dedicated bravery must be making on the people. But he was also concerned for his revered master and had earnestly implored him not to go right up close to Jahwe, and to be careful of the streams of lava running down the mountainside. However, he said, he would visit him now and again, so that the master might not lack for necessities in the God-possessed desert.

18. Accordingly Moses crossed the wilderness on his staff, his wide-set eyes bent on the mount of God, which was smoking like a chimney and often spewing out fire. It had an odd shape, the mountain: cracks and ridges ran round it, seeming to divide it into several storeys. They looked like paths running round it, but they were not: only terrace-like gradations with yellow rear walls. By the third day the pilgrim had crossed the foot-hills to the rugged base; now he began to climb, his fist closed round his staff, which he set before him as he mounted the pathless, trackless, blackened, scalded waste. Hours and hours he mounted, pace by pace, higher and higher into the nearness of God; as far as ever a human being could. For after a while the sulphurous vapours, smelling like hot metal, so filled the air that he gasped for breath and began to cough. Yet he got up to the topmost ridge just below the peak, where there was an extended view on both sides over the bare desert range and beyond the wilderness toward Kadesh. He could even see the little tribal encampment, closer in and far down in the depths.

Here Moses, coughing, found a cavity in the mountain wall, with a roof formed by a ledge of rock that should protect him from flying stones and molten streams. Here he set up his rest and took time to get his breath. And now he prepared to embark upon the task which God had laid upon him. Under all the difficulties (the metallic vapours oppressed his chest and even made the water taste of sulphur), the work was to take him forty days and forty nights.

But why so long? The question is an idle one. God's whole moral law, in permanently compact and compendious form, binding to all time, had to be composed and graven on the stone of His own mountain, in order that Moses might carry it down to his father's crude, confused, bewildered folk, down to the enclosure where they were waiting. It should be among them, from generation to generation inviolably graven as well in their minds and hearts and their flesh and blood, the quintessence of human good behaviour. God commanded him loudly from out of his own breast to hew two tables from the living rock and write the decrees on them, five on one and five on the other — in all, ten decrees. To make the tablets, to smooth them and shape them to be adequate bearers of the eternal law — that in itself was no small thing. One man alone, even though he had broad wrists and had drunk the milk of a stone-mason's daughter, might not for many days accomplish it. Actually the making of the tables took a quarter of the forty days. But the writing itself, when he came to it, was a problem that might well bring Moses' stay on the hill-top to more than forty days. For how was he to write? In his Theban boarding-school he had learned the decorative picture writing of the Egyptians and its cursive adaptation; also the cramped cuneiform of the formal script practised in the region of the Euphrates and employed by the kings of the earth to exchange ideas on earthen shards. And among the Midianites he had got acquainted with a third kind of semantic magic expressed in symbols, such as eyes, crosses, beetles, rings, and various kinds of wavy lines. This kind of writing was used in the land of Sinai; it was a clumsy attempt to imitate Egyptian picture writing, but it did not manage to symbolize whole words and things — only syllables to be read together. Moses saw that no one of these three methods of putting down ideas would serve in the present case, for the simple reason that all of them depended on the language they expressed by signs. Not in Babylonian or Egyptian or the jargon of the Beduins of Sinai — not in any one of these could he possibly write down the ten decrees. No, they must and could only be written in the tongue of the fathers' seed — the idiom it spoke, the dialect he himself used in his formative task; and that no matter whether they could read it or not. Indeed, how should they read it, when it could scarcely be written and there did not yet exist any semantic magic whatever for the tongue they talked in?

Fervently, with all his heart, Moses wished for it: for a kind of simple writing that they would be able to read quite quickly; one that they, children as they were, could learn in a few days — and it followed that such a one, God's help being nigh, could also be thought out and invented in no longer time. For thought out and invented a kind of writing had got to be, since it did not exist.

What a pressing, oppressive task! He had not measured it beforehand. He had thought only of "writing" — not at all of the fact that one could not just "write." His head glowed and steamed like a furnace; it was like the top of the peak itself, on fire with the fervour of his hopes for his people. He felt as though rays streamed from his head; as though horns came out on his brow for very strain of desire and pure inspiration. He could not invent signs for all the words his people used, nor for the syllables which composed them. The vocabulary of the people down there in the camp was small enough. But even so it would need so many symbols that they could not be invented in the limited number of days at his command; much less could the people learn to read them. So Moses contrived something else — and horns stood forth from his head out of sheer pride of his god-invention. He classified the sounds of the language: those made with the lips, with the tongue and palate, and with the throat; and he divided off from them the smaller group of open sounds which became words only when they were included in combinations with the others. Of those others there were not so very many — a bare twenty; and if you gave them signs which regularly obliged anyone pronouncing them to buzz or hiss, to huff or puff, or mumble or rumble, then you might adapt your sounds and combine them into words and pictures of things, paying no heed to those in the other group, which came in automatically anyhow. You could make as many combinations as you liked, and that not only in the language spoken by his father's people, but in any language whatever. You could even write Egyptian and Babylonian with them.

A god-inspiration! An inspiration with horns to it! It was like to its source, to the Invisible and Spiritual whence it came, who possessed all the world, and who, though He had especially elected the stock down below for His own, yet He was Lord everywhere and all over on earth. But it was also an inspiration peculiarly apt for Moses' immediate and urgent purpose and for the necessity out of which it was born — for the brief and binding text of the law. Of course, this was first to be impressed upon the seed which Moses had led out of Egypt, because God and he had a common love to it. But just as the handful of arbitrary signs might be used to write down all the words of all the tongues of all the people on earth, and just as Jahwe was omnipotent over all these, so also the text which Moses intended to set down by means of those signs should likewise be universal. It should be a compendium of such a kind as to serve everywhere on earth and to all the peoples on it as a foundation stone of morality and good conduct.

So, then, Moses — his head on fire — began by scratching his signs on the rocky wall in loose imitation of the sounds the Sinai people made, conjuring them up in his mind as he went. With his graving tool he scratched on the rock the signs he had made to represent the burrs and purrs and whirrs, the hisses and buzzes, the humming and gurgling of his father's native tongue. He set them down in an order that pleased his ear — and lo, with them one could set down the whole world in writing: the signs that took up space and those that took none, the derived and the contrived — in short, everything on earth.

And he wrote; I mean, he drilled and chiselled and scooped at the splintery stone of the tables; for these he had prepared beforehand with great pains, during the time he had spent cogitating his script. The whole took him rather more than forty days — and no wonder!

Young Joshua came up to him a few times, to fetch water and bread. The people did not need to know this: they believed that Moses sojourned up there sustained solely by God's presence and His words, and Joshua for strategic reasons preferred them to remain in this belief.

Moses rose with the dawn and laboured till the sun set back in the desert. We must picture him there, sitting bare to the waist, his breast hairy, with the strong arms bequeathed him by his father the slain water-bearer; with wide-set eyes, flattened nose, and parted grizzling beard; chewing a pancake, coughing now and then from the metallic vapours, and in the sweat of his brow hewing at the tables, filing and planing. Squatting before them as he leaned against the rocky wall, he toiled away with great attention to detail; first drawing his pot-hooks, his magic runes, with the graver and then drilling them into the stone.

He wrote on the first table:

I, Jahwe, am thy God; thou shalt have no other gods before me.

Thou shalt not make unto thyself any graven image.

Thou shalt not take my name in vain.

Be mindful of my day to keep it holy.

Honour thy father and thy mother.

Thou shalt not kill.

Thou shalt not commit adultery.

Thou shalt not steal.

Thou shalt not affront thy neighbour by bearing false witness.

Thou shalt not cast a covetous eye upon thy neighbour's goods.

This was what he wrote, leaving out the vowels, which were taken for granted. And while he worked it seemed to him as though rays like a pair of horns stood out from the hair of his brow.

When Joshua came up for the last time he stayed a little longer than before, in fact, two whole days, for Moses was not done with his work, and they wanted to go down together. The youth admired and warmly praised what his master had done, consoling him in the matter of a few letters which, despite all Moses' loving care and greatly to his distress, had got splintered and were illegible. Joshua assured him that the general effect was unharmed.

As a finishing touch in Joshua's presence Moses coloured the letters he had engraved. He did it with his own blood, that they might stand out better. No other colouring matter was at hand; so he pricked his strong arm with the tool and carefully let the drops of blood run into the outlines of the letters, so that they showed red against the stone. When the script was dry, Moses took a table under each arm, handed to the young man the staff which had supported him on his climb; and so they went down together from the mountain of God to the tribal encampment opposite in the desert.

19.

When they had got within hearing of the enclosure, though still fairly far off, there came to their ears a distant squalling which they knew not how to explain. Moses heard it first, but it was Joshua who spoke of it.

"Do you hear those strange sounds?" he asked, " — all that noise and hubbub? There is something the matter, I think; some kind of brawl, if I am not mistaken. And it must be considerable, and violent, for us to hear it from where we are. If it is as I think, then it is a good thing you are getting back."

"It is a good thing in any case," answered Moses. "But so far as I can make out, that is not a brawling I hear, but a noise of merry-making, with something like singing and dancing. Don't you hear shrill yells among the bass, and crashing drums? Joshua, how do they come to be having a feast without my permission? Joshua, what has got into them? Let us hasten our steps."

He hoisted up his tables under his arm-pits and stepped out faster, and Joshua strode alongside, shaking his head. "Singing and dancing, singing and dancing," he repeated, more and more dismayed, at length in sheer alarm. For by now they could tell that this was no rough-and-tumble. They were not scuffling, one on top and one underneath. No, they were bawling in chorus. The only question was, what sort of song they were bawling.

Even that riddle was soon resolved. It was a most dreadful state of affairs. When Moses and Joshua hastened under the beam of the gate and entered the enclosure, they could see it in all its bald shamelessness. The tribes were out of bounds. They had flung aside all restraint, all the precepts which Moses had laid upon them for their souls' good, and all godly decorum. They had reverted, in short, and were wallowing with hair-raising abandon.

Just beyond the gate was an open assembly-place; this was now the theatre where they were celebrating their miserable freedom. They had all gorged their fill before the singing and dancing; the open space betrayed to any eye the marks of slaughtering and gluttony. And in honour of what had they slaughtered and stuffed? It was standing there. In the centre of the open space, on a stone plinth, an altar base, an image stood, a crudely made thing, a misbegotten idol, a gilded calf.

It was no calf: it was a bull, the common stud bull of all the peoples of the world. It has been called a calf because it was only medium-sized, even rather small, badly cast, and ridiculously shaped, a clumsy abomination, but only too easily recognizable as the bull it was. Around the clumsy invention moved a ring a dozen deep, men and women hand in hand, dancing to the sound of cymbals and drums. Their heads were flung back, their eyes rolled up, their knees tossed up to their chins; they squalled, shouted and made coarse gestures of worship towards the image. They went round in opposite directions, one shameful circle moving to the right, the next to the left. And inside the inmost ring, in front of the calf, Aaron could be seen hopping up and down in the long-sleeved garment he wore in the service of the tabernacle; he had pulled it up so as to be able to fling his long, hairy legs the better. And Miriam, shaking her timbrel, was leading the women in the dance.

So much for the ring about the calf. In the space round about it there was fitting accompaniment to the sight. It is painful to describe the shamelessness that was there. Some were eating blindworms. Others were lying with their sisters, and that in public, in honour of the calf. Others again simply squatted and relieved themselves, guiltless of any little trowel. One saw men offering their strength to the bull. Somewhere a man was cuffing his own mother, right and left.

At this horrid sight Moses' angry vein swelled to bursting. With blazing face he pushed his way straight up to the calf, bursting through the ring of dancers, who came staggering to a stop and goggled at him with embarrassed grins as they recognized the master. He went straight to the heart, the source, the monstrous core of the crime. He lifted high one of the tables of the law in his mighty arms and smashed it down upon the ridiculous animal until it buckled at the knees; struck again and again with such fury that the tablet itself flew into pieces and the effigy was an almost formless mass. He swung the other table and gave the death blow to the abomination, smashing it utterly; and as the second tablet was still whole, he broke it upon the stone base. Then he stood there with quivering fists and groaned from the depths of his heart.

"You debased, you god-forsaken wretches! There lies what I brought you down from God and what He wrote for you with His own finger to be a talisman against your miserable state of ignorance. There it lies in bits among the ruins of your idol. What shall I do with you now before the Lord, that He consume you not?"

And he saw Aaron, who had been hopping up and down, standing near him with his eyes cast down and his greasy curls in his neck, inexpressibly awkward and foolish. Moses took him by the clothes in front and shook him, saying:

"How comes the gilded Belial here, the filthy beast? And what had the people done to you that you thrust them down to ruin while I was on the mountain, and even prance and wanton before him yourself, as though you were a goat?"

But Aaron answered: "Ah, my dear lord, let not your wrath mount up against me and your sister, for we were forced to yield. You know the wickedness of this people; verily, they forced us. You stayed away too long and stopped on the mountain an eternity, so that we all thought you were never coming back. Then the people assembled against me and shrieked: 'No one knows what has become of this Moses man who led us out of Egypt. He will not be coming back. Probably the jaws of the mountain, out of which it spews, have swallowed him up. Up, then, make us gods which can go before us when Amalek returns! We are a people like another, and we want to wanton before gods which are like other peoples' gods!' Thus they spake, my lord, for, by your leave, they thought they were rid of you. But tell me what I could have done when they got together against me? I told them to bring me all their gold earrings from their ears, and I melted them down and made a mould and cast the little calf for a god to them."

"And it was not even a good likeness," said Moses contemptuously.

"I was in such haste!" Aaron replied. "For even on the next

day, that is to say today, they wanted to have their debauchery before good fleshly gods that they could understand. So I turned the cast over to them, and you cannot assert that it has no likeness at all; and they were glad, and said: 'These are your gods, O Israel, who have led you out of Egypt.' And we built an altar, and they made burnt offerings and thank offerings, and they ate, and then they played and danced a little."

Moses left him where he stood and pushed back through the broken circle to the gate, where he placed himself under the cross-beam with Joshua and cried with all his strength:

"To me, to me, all ye who belong to the Lord!" Then came many to him who were sound at heart and had joined unwillingly, and Joshua's youthful hosts gathered round the two.

"Unhappy creatures," said Moses, "what have you done, and how shall I atone for your sin before Jahwe that He may not reject you as incorrigibly evil and consume you altogether? To make to yourself a gilded Belial the minute my back is turned! Shame upon you — and upon me! Look at the ruins there! I don't mean the calf, may perdition seize it: I mean the broken pieces! They are the present I brought down to you: the everlasting, the brief and binding law, the rock of right and decency. They are the decalogue which, together with God, I wrote for you in your script and wrote it in my own blood; with the blood of my father, with your blood, I wrote it. Now lies it there, that I brought, broken in fragments."

Many of them wept, and there was a great sobbing and sniffing in all the place.

"Perhaps it can be made good," said Moses. "For the Lord is long-suffering and of great mercy, and He forgives ill doing and transgression — and lets no one go unpunished!" he suddenly thundered, his blood rushing to his head and his vein swelling up. "For I will visit the ill-doing unto the third and fourth generation, like the zealot I am. Here shall judgement be held and a bloody purification, for with blood was it written. The ringleaders shall be put to death, who first shrieked for the gilded calf and wantonly asserted that the calf led you out of Egypt, whereas it was I alone who did it — so saith the Lord. They shall be given to the avenging angel, let them be who they may. They shall be stoned to death and die by shooting — and even were there three hundred of them! But the rest shall put away all adornments and mourn until I return. For I will go again upon the mount of God and see what I can still do for you, O froward and perverse generation!"

20. Moses was not present at the executions which he had decreed on account of the calf; they were the business of the iron-handed Joshua. He himself was again on the mountain, in front of his cave under the echoing peak, while the people mourned; and he remained another forty days and forty nights up there alone in the poisonous vapours. But why so long, the second time? The answer is: It was not only because Jahwe directed him to make the tables again, and again to write the decrees on them. This time it went a bit faster, as he had had practice, and, even more important, he already had the script. No: it was because, before the Lord granted the renewal, Moses had a long struggle with Him — a wrestling in which anger and mercy, love and disgust fought together, and Moses had to use great persuasive powers and shrewd appeals to keep God from declaring the bond broken and disowning the incorrigible crew, destroying them altogether even as Moses in his wrath had destroyed the tables.

"I will not draw near to them," said God, "to lead them into the land of their fathers; do not ask it of Me, for I could not trust my patience. I am a zealot, and My wrath blazes up, and you shall see how some day I shall know Myself no more and devour them utterly."

And since the people were like the gilded calf, so badly cast and without hope of betterment, there was nothing left but to shatter and destroy them. He told Moses they should be destroyed root and branch as they stood. But that He would make him, Moses, a great people and live with him in the Covenant. But Moses could not bear it, and he said: "No, Lord, forgive them their sins; if not, then blot me too out of your book, for I will not survive and become a chosen people in my own person instead of them."

And he put God on His honour and said: "Consider, Holy One: if you slay these people as one man, then the heathen when they hear will cry, 'Fie upon the Lord! For He could not lead the people to the Promised Land as He had sworn — He was not able — and therefore has He slain them in the wilderness.' Will you have such things said of you by the peoples of the world? Therefore now let the might of the Lord wax great and be gracious to the transgression of these people in Thy mercy."

It was particularly with this argument that Moses won over the Lord and decided Him for forgiveness, even though with reservations. God declared that none of this generation should see the land of the fathers, excepting only Joshua and Caleb. "Your children," so the Lord decreed, "I will lead in. But those now more than twenty years old shall not see the Land, but their bodies shall lie down in the waste."

And Moses assented and agreed with the Lord that they would leave it at that. For the decision really coincided with his and Joshua's own purposes, so he did not argue against it. "Let me now renew the tables," he said, "and bring down to the tribes Thy brief and binding will. After all, it was no great loss that I broke the first ones: there were a few bad letters in them. I will confess to You now that I thought of it when I smashed them."

So he sat there a second time, with his food and drink secretly supplied by Joshua. He sharpened and chiselled, planed and smoothed, sat and wrote, wiping his brow with the back of his hand, drilling and graving the script into the tables, which were even better than the first ones. And afterwards he once more painted the letters with his blood. Then he descended the hill with the Law under his arms.

Israel had been notified that it should end its mourning and should put on festal garments — of course excepting their earrings, for those had been melted down to an evil end. And all the people came before Moses that he might give them what he had brought: the message of Jahwe from the mountain, the tables with the decalogue.

"Take them, O blood of my father," he said, "and keep them holy in God's tent. But that which they say, that keep holy yourselves in doing and in leaving undone. For it is the brief and binding, the condensed will of God, the bed-rock of all good behaviour and breeding, and God wrote it in the stone with my little graving tool — the Alpha and Omega of human decency. In your speech He wrote it, but in signs with which if necessary all the languages of the world can be written; for He is Lord everywhere. Hence this ABC is His, and His speech, though it be addressed to you, O Israel, yet it is just as much an universal speech.

"In the stone of the mountains I engraved the ABC of human conduct, but no less shall it be graven in your flesh and blood, O Israel, so that everyone who breaks one of the ten commandments shall shrink within himself and before God, and it shall be cold about his heart because he overstepped God's bound. Well I know, and God He too knows well, that His commands will not be obeyed, but will be rebelled against over and over again. But everyone who breaks the laws shall from now on grow icy cold about the heart, because they are written in his flesh and blood and he knows the Word will avail.

"But cursed be the man who stands up and says: 'They are good no longer.' Cursed be he who teaches you: 'Up and be free of them, lie, steal, and slay, whore, dishonour father and mother and give them to the knife, and you shall praise my name because I proclaim freedom to you.' Cursed be he who sets up a calf and says: 'There is your God. To its honour do all this, and lead a new dance about it.' Your God will be very strong; on a golden chair will he sit and pass for the wisest because he knows the ways of the human heart are evil from youth upwards. But that will be all that he knows; and he who only knows that is as stupid as the night is black, and better it were for him had he never been born. For he knows not of the bond between God and man, which none can break, neither man nor God, for it is inviolate. Blood will flow in streams because of his black stupidity, so that the red pales from the cheek of mankind, but there is no help, for the base must be cut down. And I will lift up My foot, saith the Lord, and tread him into the mire — to the bottom of the earth will I tread the blasphemer, an hundred and twelve fathoms deep, and man and beast shall make a bend around the spot where I trod him in, and the birds of the air high in their flight shall swerve that they fly not over it. And whosoever names his name shall spit towards the four quarters of the earth, and wipe his mouth and say 'God save us all!' that the earth may be again the earth — a vale of troubles, but not a sink of iniquity. Say Amen to that!" And

all
the
people
said
Amen.

This book is composed on the Linotype in
Bodoni, so called after Giambattista
Bodoni (1740–1813), son of a printer of
Piedmont. After gaining experience and
fame as superintendent of the Press of the
Propaganda in Rome, Bodoni became in
1766 the head of the ducal printing house
at Parma, which he soon made the foremost
of its kind in Europe. His Manuale
Tipografico, completed by his widow in
1818, contains 279 pages of specimens of
types, including alphabets of about thirty
foreign languages. His editions of Greek,
Latin, Italian, and French classics, especially his Homer, are celebrated for their
typography. In type-designing he was an
innovator, making his new faces rounder,
wider, and lighter, with greater openness
and delicacy. His types were rather too
rigidly perfect in detail, the thick lines
contrasting sharply with the thin wiry lines.
Bodoni Book, as reproduced by the Linotype
Company, is a modern version based, not
upon any one of Bodoni's fonts, but upon a
composite conception of the Bodoni manner,
designed to avoid the details stigmatized as
bad by typographical experts and to secure
the pleasing and effective results of which
the Bodoni types are capable.

The book was composed, printed, and
bound by THE PLIMPTON PRESS, Norwood,
Mass. The typographic scheme and binding
and jacket design are by Paul Rand.

This book has been produced in full
compliance with all government regulations
for the conservation of paper, metal, and
other essential materials.